The last track of the shimmying nosewheel of an aircraft.

STABILITY CRITERIA
FOR LINEAR
DYNAMICAL SYSTEMS

B. PORTER

M.A., Ph.D., C.Eng., A.M.I.Mech.E.,
Reader in Engineering Dynamics
University of Newcastle upon Tyne

1968

ACADEMIC PRESS   NEW YORK/LONDON

ACADEMIC PRESS INC
111 Fifth Avenue
New York, New York 10003

Library of Congress Catalog Card Number 68-19694

Printed in Great Britain

'It will be seen that the motion of a machine with its governor consists in general of a uniform motion, combined with a disturbance which may be expressed as the sum of several component motions. These components may be of four different kinds:

(i)   The disturbance may continually increase.

(ii) It may continually diminish.

(iii) It may be an oscillation of continually increasing amplitude.

(iv) It may be an oscillation of continually decreasing amplitude.

The first and third cases are evidently inconsistent with stability of the motion; and the second and fourth alone are admissible in a good governor. This condition is mathematically equivalent to the condition that all the possible roots, and all the possible parts of the impossible roots, of a certain equation shall be negative.

I have not been able completely to determine these conditions for equations of a higher degree than the third; but I hope that the subject will obtain the attention of mathematicians.'

J. C. Maxwell, 'On Governors',
Proc. R. Soc., **16**, 270, 1868.

PREFACE

In the century that has elapsed since the problem of determining adequate criteria of dynamical stability was posed to mathematicians by J. C. Maxwell, numerous methods of analysing system stability have been developed and stability theory has become one of the most intensively cultivated fields of applied mathematics. Indeed, so many stability criteria are now available that engineering students are often confused by their very profusion. This situation is exacerbated by the fact that most engineering textbooks present stability criteria as rather arbitrary algorithms which have to be accepted without proof and learnt by rote: the mathematical foundations of such criteria are very rarely discussed in any detail. Paradoxically, this dearth of complete information is particularly acute in regard to the relatively simple (but very useful) stability criteria which have been developed for the analysis of *linearisable* systems and which are now such an important ingredient of most undergraduate engineering curricula in applied dynamics and automatic control.

The present book is an attempt to remedy this situation and accordingly has two principal objects:

(i) to provide a collation of those stability criteria which are considered to be most useful in the analysis of linearisable mechanical engineering systems;

(ii) to explain the mathematical bases of the principal criteria in simple terms so that they can be better understood and more effectively used.

It should be noted that this book is thus primarily concerned with the analysis of system governing equations and not with the techniques for setting up such equations or with the qualitative description of actual cases of instability which have occurred in practice. However, the governing equations of a number of specific systems are used to illustrate the general theory and, in many instances, the merits of alternative stability criteria are compared by analysing the same system by different methods. In addition, the sets of problems which are appended to Chapters 2–9 involve the application of the analytical techniques to a number of practical systems.

The results presented in this book are, of course, the collective output of numerous engineers and mathematicians. However, no attempt has been made to provide a complete bibliography of all the pertinent publications but instead only key references are cited in the text. Of these, the works of F. R. Gantmacher and M. A. Aizerman were particularly useful in writing this book.

In view of the fact that real systems are never truly linear, it is remarkable that so much useful information regarding the stability of engineering systems can be obtained on the basis of linearised theories of the kind presented in this book. However, systems do, of course, exist which are strictly non-linearisable and whose behaviour can be predicted only on the basis of more complicated theories that take full account of their non-linearity. Such theories lie outside the scope of the present book and readers wishing to extend their studies into the non-linear domain should begin by consulting a book on Liapunov's methods such as that by J. P. Lasalle and S. Lefschetz, *Stability by Liapunov's Direct Method with Applications*, Academic Press, 1961.

I am grateful to Professor D. C. Johnson for encouraging me to write this text and for reading substantial sections of the original manuscript; to Professor L. Maunder for scrutinising the final draft; and to Professor A. F. Burstall for supporting the project and facilitating its completion in many ways. I am also indebted to the Institution of Mechanical Engineers for permission to include Figs. 1.1, 1.2 and 8.6, and to the American Air Force for permission to reproduce the photograph which forms the frontispiece.

Department of Mechanical Engineering,   B. P.
University of Newcastle upon Tyne.

CONTENTS

ix

Chapter 5

HURWITZ'S CRITERION

Chapter 6

ROOT-LOCI

Chapter 7

METHOD OF D-PARTITION

Chapter 8

STABILITY OF SYSTEMS GOVERNED BY
DIFFERENTIAL-DIFFERENCE EQUATIONS

Chapter 9

STABILITY OF SYSTEMS HAVING
PERIODICALLY VARYING PARAMETERS

Chapter 1

INTRODUCTION

It is usual to regard an equilibrium state of a dynamical system as being *unstable* if, when disturbed from this state of equilibrium, the system diverges from its original configuration: on the other hand, if a system returns to the neighbourhood of its original equilibrium state after a disturbance, it is regarded as being *stable*. Dynamical instability is of great practical significance since it is a dominant and usually undesirable feature of the behaviour of many engineering systems. Thus, for example, under certain conditions a machine-tool may 'chatter', an automobile wheel may 'shimmy', an aircraft wing may 'flutter', or a closed-loop automatic control system may 'hunt' with increasing amplitude until either failure occurs or the motion is limited by the presence of nonlinearities. In designing systems of this type it is therefore essential to choose the dynamical parameters so as to avoid the possible occurrence of unstable behaviour.

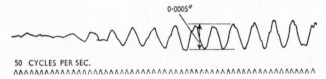

Fig. 1.1. Build-up of chatter in a radial drilling machine.

Typical unstable motions are illustrated in Fig. 1.1, which is a record of the build-up of chatter in a radial drilling machine,† and in Fig. 1.2, which shows records of fully developed hunting in the closed-loop water-level control system for a feed-water deaerator.‡ The frontispiece is a photograph of the last track of the shimmying nosewheel of an aircraft.

In a stability analysis, as in any kind of engineering investigation, the first step is to replace the actual system by an idealised system which nevertheless exhibits the salient features of the behaviour of the original.

† S. A. Tobias and W. Fishwick, The vibrations of radial-drilling machines under test and working conditions, *Proc. Instn mech. Engrs*, **170**, 232, 1956.

‡ A. J. Morton, Hunting of water level in float-controlled deaerators, *Proc. Instn mech. Engrs*, **173**, 735, 1959.

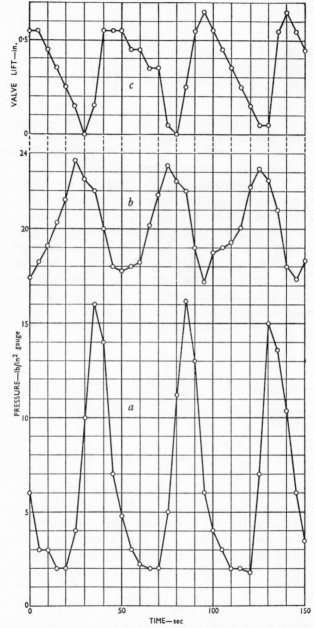

Fig. 1.2. Records of fully developed hunting in a feed-water deaerator: (*a*) heatingsteam pressure; (*b*) feed inlet pressure; (*c*) valve lift.

Now, in reality, all physical systems have an infinite number of degrees of freedom and are governed by *partial* differential equations. However, in order to facilitate analysis it is usual to represent a real system by an approximate mathematical model having a finite number of degrees of freedom. This is done by 'lumping' at a number of discrete points those physical properties of the system which are actually distributed throughout regions of space: the resulting model is governed by *ordinary* differential (or differential-difference) equations. Thus, for example, it is possible to analyse the transverse vibrations of a beam of complicated non-uniform section by 'lumping' the distributed mass of the beam at a finite number of points whilst leaving the elastic properties of the beam unchanged.

The next stage in the approximate analysis of a real system is the investigation of its 'lumped'-parameter model. However, it is frequently found that this model is nonlinear and that, in the case of an unstable system, the nonlinearity becomes non-negligible for large excursions from equilibrium. Since general solutions are known only for a few relatively simple nonlinear differential equations, it follows that the complete analysis of even a 'lumped'-parameter model is rarely possible. However, an engineer concerned with dynamical stability is normally not so much interested in the ultimate nonlinear response of a system as in predicting those conditions under which unstable motions will tend to build up, so that such motions can be avoided. This information can usually be found by linearising the governing equations of the 'lumped'-parameter model (on the assumption that its motions are initially small) and then testing the stability of the resulting approximate equations of motion by criteria of the type presented in this book.† Of course, if predictions regarding the ultimate nonlinear response of a system in an unstable régime were required, it would be necessary to revert to the nonlinear equations and attempt to obtain their solutions either numerically or by approximate analytical methods.

These remarks on linearisation can be illustrated by considering van der Pol's equation

$$\frac{d^2x}{dt^2} - \varepsilon(1 - x^2)\frac{dx}{dt} + x = 0. \tag{1.1}$$

This is nonlinear when $\varepsilon \neq 0$ because of the presence of the term in

† This follows from a theorem of Liapunov which indicates that the stability of a linearised system implies the stability of the corresponding equilibrium configuration of the non-linear 'lumped'-parameter model, except when the characteristic equation of the linearised system has imaginary roots.

$x^2(dx/dt)$. However, if $|x|$ is small, x^2 may be neglected in comparison with unity and the equation (1.1) is then approximately

$$\frac{d^2x}{dt^2} - \varepsilon \frac{dx}{dt} + x = 0 \qquad (1.2)$$

which is the linearised form of van der Pol's equation. It can be verified by direct substitution that equation (1.2) has a solution of the form

$$x = c_1 e^{s_1 t} + c_2 e^{s_2 t}, \qquad (1.3)$$

where c_1 and c_2 are constants of integration and s_1 and s_2 are the roots of the so-called characteristic equation

$$s^2 - \varepsilon s + 1 = 0. \qquad (1.4)$$

Now if $\varepsilon > 0$, it is evident that the roots of equation (1.4) have positive real parts. The linearised solution given by equation (1.3) therefore tends to infinity with time, thus indicating that the linearised system is unstable. It may therefore be deduced from Liapunov's theorem that the equilibrium configuration $x = 0 = dx/dt$ of a non-linear system governed by equation (1.1) will be unstable when $\varepsilon > 0$. In such cases the slightest disturbance will cause the system to diverge from its equilibrium configuration and eventually settle down into a

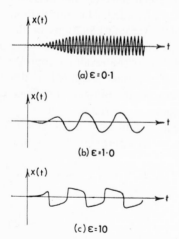

(a) $\varepsilon = 0.1$

(b) $\varepsilon = 1.0$

Fig. 1.3. Typical solutions of van der Pol's equation.

(c) $\varepsilon = 10$

steady *limit cycle* of oscillation whose amplitude can be predicted by various approximate methods of nonlinear analysis. Motions of this type are shown in Fig. 1.3 for a number of positive values of ε.

However, if $\varepsilon = 0$, equation (1.4) has imaginary roots and therefore no conclusions as to the stability of the nonlinear system may be drawn from the behaviour of the linearised system. Nevertheless, it is evident that a system governed by equation (1.1) will be stable in this case, since (1.1) has a bounded but oscillatory solution of the form $x = a \sin (t + \phi)$ when $\varepsilon = 0$. It should be noted that this oscillation differs from the limit cycle oscillation which occurs when $\varepsilon > 0$ in that the amplitude a can be made arbitrarily small by choosing the initial conditions appropriately, whereas the limit cycle amplitude is always finite and independent of the initial conditions.

Finally, if $\varepsilon < 0$, the roots of equation (1.4) have negative real parts. The linearised solution given by equation (1.3) therefore decays to zero with time, thus indicating that the linearised system is stable. It may therefore be deduced from Liapunov's theorem that the equilibrium configuration of a nonlinear system governed by van der Pol's equation is stable when $\varepsilon < 0$.

By this technique of linearising the governing equations of 'lumped'-parameter models, it is found that in most instances the stability characteristics of a real system can be adequately approximated by those of a linear system of one of the following types:

   (i)   a system having 'lumped' time-invariant parameters.

   (ii) a system having 'lumped' time-variant parameters.

Systems of the first type are governed by linear ordinary differential (or differential-difference) equations having constant coefficients, whilst those of the second are governed by equations having variable coefficients. Most of the stability criteria presented in this book concern systems of the first type having differential governing equations. However, the stability of systems governed by differential-difference equations having constant coefficients is discussed in Chapter 8, and the behaviour of systems governed by certain differential equations having periodically varying coefficients is considered in Chapter 9.

Chapter 2

RESPONSE CHARACTERISTICS
OF LINEAR SYSTEMS HAVING
TIME-INVARIANT PARAMETERS

2.1 Laplace transformation

The analysis of the stability of a linear system having 'lumped', time-invariant parameters and no finite time-delays† can be reduced to the problem of determining the nature of the roots of a certain algebraic equation known as the *characteristic equation* of the system. It is the purpose of this chapter to demonstrate the central importance of the characteristic equation and to show how it can be derived from the equations of motion of a linear system.

The behaviour of a linear system having a single input variable $y(t)$ and a single output variable $x(t)$ is governed by an ordinary differential equation of the form

$$a_0 \frac{d^n x}{dt^n} + a_1 \frac{d^{n-1} x}{dt^{n-1}} + \ldots + a_{n-1} \frac{dx}{dt} + a_n x$$

$$= b_0 \frac{d^m y}{dt^m} + b_1 \frac{d^{m-1} y}{dt^{m-1}} + \ldots + b_{m-1} \frac{dy}{dt} + b_m y, \quad (2.1)$$

where the a_r and b_r are real or complex constants. This equation can be written in the abbreviated form

$$P(D)x(t) = Q(D)y(t), \quad (2.2)$$

where

$$P(D) = a_0 D^n + a_1 D^{n-1} + \ldots + a_{n-1} D + a_n,$$

$$Q(D) = b_0 D^m + b_1 D^{m-1} + \ldots + b_{m-1} D + b_m, \quad (2.3)$$

and $D \equiv d/dt$ is the differential operator.

Although the solution of equation (2.1) can be obtained by a variety of methods, the method of Laplace transformation‡ is probably the

† Henceforth such systems will be described simply as linear systems: special designations will be used only for linear systems of other types.

‡ For more details of the Laplace transformation see, for example, M. Gardner and F. Barnes, *Transients in linear systems*, Wiley. 1942.

most convenient for the purpose of exhibiting the possible modes of response of linear systems. The Laplace transformation is an integral transformation which transforms a function $f(t)$ of the real variable t (time in the present context) into a function $F(s)$ of the complex variable $s = \sigma + i\omega$ ($i = \sqrt{-1}$) in accordance with the formula†

$$F(s) = \int_{0-}^{\infty} e^{-st} f(t) \, dt. \tag{2.4}$$

The function $F(s)$ is called the *Laplace transform* of $f(t)$, and $f(t)$ is called the *inverse Laplace transform* of $F(s)$: in symbols,

$$F(s) = \mathscr{L}[f(t)]$$

and

$$f(t) = \mathscr{L}^{-1}[F(s)].$$

It should be noted that not all functions $f(t)$ possess Laplace transforms: for, if $f(t)$ is not mathematically very well-behaved, or if it increases too rapidly as $t \to \infty$, then the integral in (2.4) will not converge and the transform $F(s)$ will not exist. However, most functions which occur in the analysis of linear systems are Laplace-transformable and moreover have transforms that can be obtained quite simply by the direct evaluation of the integral (2.4).

TABLE 2.1   Laplace transforms of common functions

	$f(t)$	$F(s) = \mathscr{L}f(t)$
1	$\delta(t)$	1
2	$u(t)$	$1/s$
3	$t^{n-1}/(n-1)!$	$1/s^n$ (n a positive integer)
4	e^{-at}	$1/(s+a)$
5	$t^{n-1} e^{-at}/(n-1)!$	$1/(s+a)^n$ (n a positive integer)
6	$\sin \omega t$	$\omega/(s^2 + \omega^2)$
7	$\cos \omega t$	$s/(s^2 + \omega^2)$
8	$e^{-at} \sin \omega t$	$\omega/\{(s+a)^2 + \omega^2\}$
9	$e^{-at} \cos \omega t$	$(s+a)/\{(s+a)^2 + \omega^2\}$

The Laplace transforms of the functions $f(t)$ most commonly encountered in the investigation of linear systems are given in Table 2.1.

† This differs from the definition given in most standard texts in that the lower limit of integration is $t = 0^-$ rather than $t = 0^+$: the present definition facilitates the transformation of impulsive functions, as is explained by F. F. Kuo, *Network analysis and synthesis*, Wiley, 1962.

In the first entry of this table, $\delta(t)$ is the *unit impulse function* defined by

$$\left.\begin{aligned}
\delta(t) &= 0, & t &\neq 0, \\
\delta(t) &= \infty, & t &= 0, \\
\int_{0-}^{0+} \delta(t)\, dt &= 1. &
\end{aligned}\right\}$$

This function is an impulse of unit strength (unit area) which is zero everywhere except at $t = 0$, where it is infinite. It can be represented graphically as the limit as $\varepsilon \to 0$ of the function shown in Fig. 2.1. In

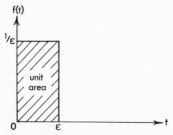

Fig. 2.1. Pulse of unit strength.

this diagram the cross-hatched rectangle becomes infinitesimally narrow and infinitely high as $\varepsilon \to 0$, whilst its area remains equal to unity. Although true impulses ($\varepsilon = 0$) are physically unrealisable, their use nevertheless facilitates the approximate analysis of systems subjected to inputs of large amplitude and short duration.

   The function $u(t)$ which appears in the second entry of Table 2.1 is the *unit step function* defined by

$$\left.\begin{aligned}
u(t) &= 0, & t &< 0, \\
u(t) &= 1, & t &\geqslant 0.
\end{aligned}\right\}$$

This function is shown in Fig. 2.2. Since $u(t)$ is discontinuous at $t = 0$, it is also physically unrealisable in the strict sense. Step functions are

Fig. 2.2. Unit step function.

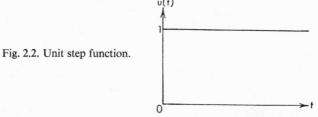

nevertheless very useful in the approximate analysis of systems suddenly subjected to changes in input from one steady value to another.

So far, the integral (2.4) has been regarded as a means of transforming *functions* of the real variable t into functions of the complex variable s. However, it is an important property of the Laplace transformation that relatively complicated *operations* in the t-domain (such as differentiation and integration) become simpler operations (such as multiplication and division by s) in the s-domain. As a result, differential equations like (2.1) can be transformed into algebraic equations which can then be easily solved for the Laplace transforms of the unknown response functions. If, finally, the process of inverse transformation is used to return to the t-domain, the required responses are obtained.

TABLE 2.2   Laplace transforms of common functional operations

	$f(t)$	$F(s) = \mathscr{L}f(t)$
1	$cf(t) \quad (c = \text{const})$	$cF(s)$
2	$f_1(t) + f_2(t)$	$F_1(s) + F_2(s)$
3	$e^{-at}f(t)$	$F(s + a)$
4	$u(t - a)f(t - a)$	$e^{-as}F(s) \quad (a \geqslant 0)$
5	$df/dt \equiv f^{(1)}(t)$	$sF(s) - f(0^-)$
6	$d^n f/dt^n \equiv f^{(n)}(t)$	$s^n F(s) - \sum\limits_{r=1}^{n} f^{(r-1)}(0^-)s^{n-r}$
7	$\int_0^t f(t)\,dt$	$F(s)/s$

The Laplace transforms of a number of common functional operations are given in Table 2.2, where the usual convention of denoting a time-function by a lower case letter and its transform by the corresponding capital letter is adopted. The first and second entries in Table 2.2 express the linearity of the Laplace transform; the third entry indicates that shifting the origin in the s-domain corresponds to multiplication by an exponential function in the t-domain; the fourth entry similarly states that shifting the origin in the t-domain corresponds to multiplication by an exponential function in the s-domain; and the last three entries indicate that, apart from initial-value terms, differentiation and integration with respect to t correspond, respectively, to multiplication and division by s. Note that in the fifth and sixth entries the argument 0^- indicates that the various functions $f^{(r-1)}(t)$ $(r = 1, 2, \ldots, n)$ are to be evaluated by letting $t \to 0$ through negative values.

2.2   Modes of transient response of single-variable systems

The technique of Laplace transformation can now be used to investigate the response characteristics of a system governed by an equation of the form (2.1). Thus, using entry 6 of Table 2.2, the transformed version of equation (2.1) is

$$(a_0 s^n + a_1 s^{n-1} + \ldots + a_{n-1}s + a_n)X(s)$$

$$= (b_0 s^m + b_1 s^{m-1} + \ldots + b_{m-1}s + b_m)Y(s)$$

$$+ a_0 \sum_{r=1}^{n} x^{(r-1)}(0^-)s^{n-r} + a_1 \sum_{r=1}^{n-1} x^{(r-1)}(0^-)s^{n-r-1} + \ldots$$

$$+ a_{n-1}x(0^-)$$

$$- b_0 \sum_{r=1}^{m} y^{(r-1)}(0^-)s^{m-r} - b_1 \sum_{r=1}^{m-1} y^{(r-1)}(0^-)s^{m-r-1} - \ldots$$

$$- b_{m-1}y(0^-), \tag{2.5}$$

where $X(s)$ and $Y(s)$ are respectively the Laplace transforms of the output $x(t)$ and the input $y(t)$. This equation has the form

$$P(s)X(s) = Q(s)Y(s) + I(s)$$

or

$$X(s) = \frac{Q(s)}{P(s)}Y(s) + \frac{I(s)}{P(s)}, \tag{2.6}$$

where the polynomials $P(s)$ and $Q(s)$ are obtained by substituting s for D in the formulae (2.3), and $I(s)$ is a polynomial whose coefficients are functions of the initial condition terms $x^{(r-1)}(0^-)$ and $y^{(r-1)}(0^-)$ such that $I(s)$ vanishes when all the initial conditions are zero (i.e., when the system is initially *quiescent*).

The response of the system to any input function $y(t)$, when the system has any set of initial conditions, can be found by obtaining the inverse Laplace transform $x(t) = \mathcal{L}^{-1}X(s)$ of the right-hand member of equation (2.6). Now although it is clear from (2.6) that the output transform $X(s)$ has two components, one depending on the input and one on the initial conditions, both components have the same denominator $P(s)$. It will transpire, that, as a result, this function largely determines the nature of the response characteristics of the system: $P(s)$ is accordingly known as the *characteristic polynomial*, and the corresponding equation

$$P(s) = a_0 s^n + a_1 s^{n-1} + \ldots + a_{n-1}s + a_n = 0 \tag{2.7}$$

is called the *characteristic equation* of the system.

If the system is initially quiescent, $I(s) = 0$ and equation (2.6) therefore becomes

$$X(s) = \frac{Q(s)}{P(s)}Y(s). \tag{2.8}$$

The function $Q(s)/P(s)$ is known as the *transfer function* of the system since equation (2.8) indicates that the effect of the quiescent system is to multiply the input transform by $Q(s)/P(s)$ to produce the output transform. This relationship between input and output can be conveniently

Fig. 2.3. Block diagram of system having one input and one output variable.

$Y(s) \longrightarrow \boxed{\dfrac{Q(s)}{P(s)}} \longrightarrow X(s)$

represented by the block diagram shown in Fig. 2.3. It should be noted that the transfer function can be formally obtained from the governing equation (2.1) by writing s in place of the operator D, putting the transforms $X(s)$ and $Y(s)$ in place of the time functions $x(t)$ and $y(t)$, and then solving for $X(s)/Y(s)$.

The response of a quiescent system to a unit impulse input $y(t) = \delta(t)$ plays an important role in stability theory and is known as the *impulse response* of the system. Since $\mathscr{L}[\delta(t)] = 1$, putting $Y(s) = 1$ in equation (2.8) shows that the Laplace transform of the impulse response of the system is given by

$$X(s) = \frac{Q(s)}{P(s)} = \frac{b_0 s^m + b_1 s^{m-1} + \ldots + b_{m-1} s + b_m}{a_0 s^n + a_1 s^{n-1} + \ldots + a_{n-1} s + a_n}. \qquad (2.9)$$

This indicates that the transfer function of a system is the Laplace transform of its impulse response: the impulse response itself can be obtained by taking the inverse transform of the last equation. In most practical systems, $m < n$ so that $Q(s)/P(s)$ is a proper rational function of s. In such cases the transfer function may be expanded in partial fractions whose denominators involve the roots of the characteristic equation $P(s) = 0$: the inverse transform of each fraction can then be found by using Table 2.1.

Thus, if $P(s) = 0$ has a real root of multiplicity p at $s = \alpha$,† the series

$$\frac{K_1}{(s - \alpha)} + \frac{K_2}{(s - \alpha)^2} + \ldots + \frac{K_p}{(s - \alpha)^p} \qquad (2.10)$$

will occur as part of the partial fraction expansion of $Q(s)/P(s)$, where the K_r are constants whose values can be obtained by the usual techniques of partial fraction expansion. Using entry 5 of Table 2.1, it is evident that

$$\mathscr{L}^{-1}\left[\frac{K_r}{(s - \alpha)^r}\right] = \frac{K_r t^{r-1} e^{\alpha t}}{(r - 1)!},$$

† This means that $P(s)$ has a factor $(s - \alpha)^p$, where α is real and $p \geqslant 1$.

and therefore that the total contribution of the terms in (2.10) to the impulse response is

$$\sum_{r=1}^{p} \left[\frac{K_r t^{r-1}}{(r-1)!} \right] e^{\alpha t}. \tag{2.11}$$

Similar contributions will of course be made by the other real roots of $P(s) = 0$.

Again, if $P(s) = 0$ has a complex root of multiplicity p at $s = \alpha + i\beta$, it may be deduced from (2.11) that the contribution of this root to the impulse response will have the form

$$\sum_{r=1}^{p} \left[\frac{K_r t^{r-1}}{(r-1)!} \right] e^{(\alpha + i\beta)t}. \tag{2.12}$$

Now, if all the coefficients in equation (2.1) are real, the complex roots of $P(s) = 0$ will occur in conjugate pairs. In such circumstances, it follows that the impulse response will also have a component

$$\sum_{r=1}^{p} \left[\frac{K_r^* t^{r-1}}{(r-1)!} \right] e^{(\alpha - i\beta)t}, \tag{2.13}$$

where K_r^* is the complex conjugate of the corresponding constant K_r which appears in (2.12). The total contribution of multiple conjugate roots at $s = \alpha \pm i\beta$ is therefore

$$\sum_{r=1}^{p} \left[\frac{(K_r e^{i\beta t} + K_r^* e^{-i\beta t}) t^{r-1}}{(r-1)!} \right] e^{\alpha t}$$

which can be written in the form

$$\sum_{r=1}^{p} \left[\frac{2\rho_r t^{r-1} \cos(\beta t + \psi_r)}{(r-1)!} \right] e^{\alpha t}, \tag{2.14}$$

where $\rho_r e^{i\psi_r} = K_r$. Similar contributions to the impulse response will be made by the other complex roots of $P(s) = 0$.

The expressions given in (2.11), (2.12), (2.13), and (2.14) represent the only types of impulse response component that can occur in linear systems having proper rational transfer functions. It is important to note that the essential properties of these response components (in particular, their behaviour as $t \to \infty$) are determined by the nature of the roots of the characteristic equation $P(s) = 0$. Moreover, since $P(s)$ is the denominator of both components of the general response transform $X(s)$ given in equation (2.6), it can be inferred that the properties of the transient response resulting from *any* type of disturbance are also largely determined by the nature of the characteristic roots: in fact, the transient response of a linear system can contain only components of the type that constitute its impulse response. It is therefore convenient (for the sake of definiteness) to characterise the transient response of a system by means of the properties of its impulse response. In particular, it is convenient to define the stability of a linear system in terms of the ultimate behaviour of its impulse response as $t \rightarrow \infty$. Such a definition will be given in Section 2.4 after the general results of the present section have been illustrated by applying them to the analysis of a number of specific systems.

2.3 Transient response of first- and second-order systems

The system shown in Fig. 2.4 consists of a massless trolley which is coupled to ground by means of a viscous dashpot whose friction con-

Fig. 2.4. First-order system.

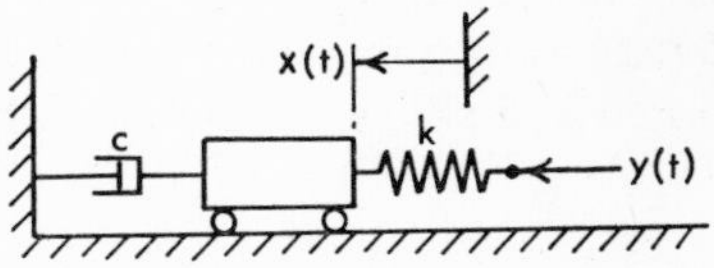

stant is c. One end of a linear spring of stiffness k is also attached to the trolley, the other end being constrained to move in a predetermined manner given by $y(t)$. If $x(t)$ is the displacement of the trolley from its position in the unstrained equilibrium configuration of the system, equating the spring and dashpot forces gives

$$k(y - x) = c \frac{dx}{dt},$$

i.e.,

$$(D + \lambda)x = \lambda y, \qquad (2.15)$$

where $\lambda = k/c$ and $D \equiv d/dt$. The last equation has the form (2.2) with $P(D) = D + \lambda$ and $Q(D) = \lambda$. Since equation (2.15) is a first-order equation, systems governed by equations of this type are known as *first-order systems*. The quantity $1/\lambda$ has the dimensions of time and is known as the *time-constant* of the system.

In order to solve equation (2.15) by means of the Laplace transformation it is necessary to use entry 5 of Table 2.2. This indicates that

$$\mathscr{L}[Dx] = sX(s) - x(0^-),$$

where $X(s)$ is the Laplace transform of $x(t)$ and $x(0^-)$ is the initial value of $x(t)$. Hence, if $Y(s)$ is the transform of the input $y(t)$, it follows that the transformed version of (2.15) is

$$sX(s) - x(0^-) + \lambda X(s) = \lambda Y(s)$$

which may be solved to give

$$X(s) = \left(\frac{\lambda}{s + \lambda}\right)Y(s) + \frac{x(0^-)}{(s + \lambda)}. \qquad (2.16)$$

The denominator of both components of the right-hand member of equation (2.16) is the characteristic polynomial $P(s) = s + \lambda$. The characteristic equation is consequently

$$P(s) = s + \lambda = 0 \qquad (2.17)$$

which has a single root $s_1 = -\lambda$. This root always lies on the real axis in the left half of the s-plane since $\lambda = k/c$ is a positive real parameter for the present system. In fact if λ increases from 0 to $+\infty$, the characteristic root traces out the whole of the negative real axis between the origin and $s = -\infty$, as is shown in Fig. 2.5. The negative real axis is

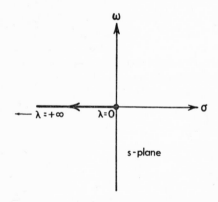

Fig. 2.5. Root-locus diagram for first-order system.

accordingly known as the *root-locus* for the first-order system. Of course, if λ could become negative, the characteristic root $s_1 = -\lambda$ would become positive and the corresponding root-locus would occupy the positive real axis.

If the system is quiescent when subjected to an input $y(t)$, then $x(0^-) = 0$ and equation (2.16) becomes

$$X(s) = \left(\frac{\lambda}{s + \lambda}\right)Y(s). \qquad (2.18)$$

This indicates that the transfer function of the first-order system is

$\lambda/(s + \lambda)$. The relationship between the input and output transforms can therefore be represented by the block-diagram shown in Fig. 2.6.

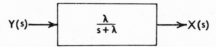

Fig. 2.6. Block diagram of first-order system.

If the input is a unit impulse, $Y(s) = \mathcal{L}[\delta(t)] = 1$ and equation (2.18) gives

$$X(s) = \frac{\lambda}{s + \lambda}$$

as the transform of the impulse response. According to entry 4 of Table 2.1, the impulse response itself is therefore†

$$x(t) = \lambda e^{-\lambda t}. \tag{2.19}$$

This indicates that, in accordance with the general theory of the last section, the impulse response is essentially an exponential function of the form $e^{\alpha t}$, where $\alpha = -\lambda$ is the root of the characteristic equation (2.17).

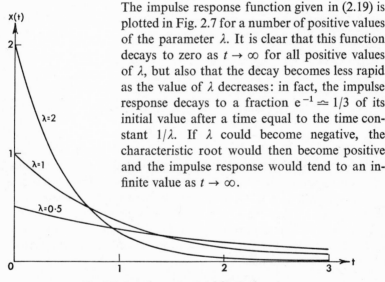

The impulse response function given in (2.19) is plotted in Fig. 2.7 for a number of positive values of the parameter λ. It is clear that this function decays to zero as $t \to \infty$ for all positive values of λ, but also that the decay becomes less rapid as the value of λ decreases: in fact, the impulse response decays to a fraction $e^{-1} \simeq 1/3$ of its initial value after a time equal to the time constant $1/\lambda$. If λ could become negative, the characteristic root would then become positive and the impulse response would tend to an infinite value as $t \to \infty$.

Fig. 2.7. Impulse response of first-order system.

In order to demonstrate that the transient response following any disturbance has the same form as (2.19), now suppose that the system

† Note that there is a discontinuity in $x(t)$ at $t = 0$; for equation (2.19) implies that $x(0^+) = \lambda$, whereas it is postulated that $x(0^-) = 0$.

is not subjected to impulsive excitation but is instead disturbed so that $x(0^-)$ has an arbitrary non-zero value and $Y(s) = 0$. It follows from equation (2.16) that the Laplace transform of the function describing the resulting motion is

$$X(s) = \frac{x(0^-)}{(s + \lambda)}.$$

Inverse transformation of this equation yields

$$x(t) = x(0^-)e^{-\lambda t},$$

which has the same form as the impulse response function given by the expression (2.19).

As a second illustration of the general theory of the last section, consider the system shown in Fig. 2.8. This is the same as that shown in

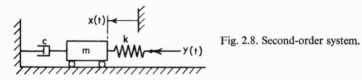

Fig. 2.8. Second-order system.

Fig. 2.4 except that the trolley is now assumed to have a mass m. At any time t, Newton's second law requires that

$$m\frac{d^2x}{dt^2} = k(y - x) - c\frac{dx}{dt},$$

i.e.,

$$(D^2 + 2v\omega_n D + \omega_n^2)x = \omega_n^2 y, \tag{2.20}$$

where $\omega_n^2 = k/m$, $2v\omega_n = c/m$, and $D \equiv d/dt$. The last equation has the form (2.2) with $P(D) = D^2 + 2v\omega_n D + \omega_n^2$ and $Q(D) = \omega_n^2$. Since (2.20) is a second-order equation, systems having this type of governing equation are known as *second-order systems*. The quantity v is a dimensionless damping parameter and, as will become apparent later, ω_n is the frequency of free undamped vibrations of the system.

The modes of transient response of the second-order system can be analysed by taking the Laplace transform of equation (2.20). Entry 6 of Table 2.2 indicates that

$$\mathscr{L}[Dx] = sX(s) - x(0^-),$$

and

$$\mathscr{L}[D^2x] = s^2 X(s) - sx(0^-) - x^{(1)}(0^-),$$

where $X(s)$ is the Laplace transform of $x(t)$, and $x(0^-)$ and $x^{(1)}(0^-)$ are respectively the initial values of $x(t)$ and its first derivative. Hence, if $Y(s)$ is the transform of the input $y(t)$, it follows that the transformed version of equation (2.20) is

$$s^2 X(s) - sx(0^-) - x^{(1)}(0^-) + 2v\omega_n[sX(s) - x(0^-)]$$
$$+ \omega_n^2 X(s) = \omega_n^2 Y(s)$$

which can be solved for $X(s)$ to give

$$X(s) = \left(\frac{\omega_n^2}{s^2 + 2v\omega_n s + \omega_n^2}\right) Y(s)$$
$$+ \left(\frac{(s + 2v\omega_n)x(0^-) + x^{(1)}(0^-)}{s^2 + 2v\omega_n s + \omega_n^2}\right). \quad (2.21)$$

As in the case of the first-order system, the output transform of the second-order system given by equation (2.21) has one component which depends on the input and one which depends on the initial conditions. The characteristic polynomial $P(s) = s^2 + 2v\omega_n s + \omega_n^2$ is the denominator of both components, and the characteristic equation of the second-order system is accordingly

$$P(s) = s^2 + 2v\omega_n s + \omega_n^2 = 0. \quad (2.22)$$

If the system is quiescent when subjected to an input $y(t)$, then $x(0^-) = 0 = x^{(1)}(0^-)$ and equation (2.21) becomes

$$X(s) = \left(\frac{\omega_n^2}{s^2 + 2v\omega_n s + \omega_n^2}\right) Y(s). \quad (2.23)$$

This indicates that the transfer function of the second-order system is $\omega_n^2/(s^2 + 2v\omega_n s + \omega_n^2)$ and that the relationship between input and output transforms can be represented by the block-diagram shown in

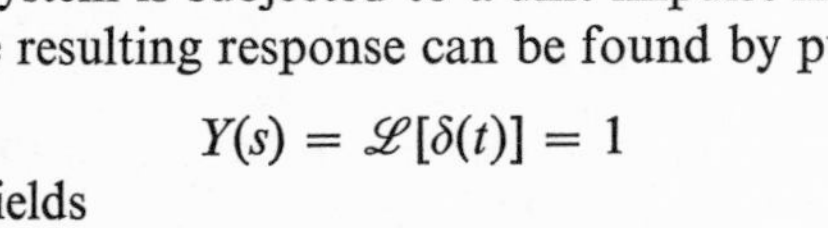

Fig. 2.9. Block diagram of second-order system.

Fig. 2.9. If the system is subjected to a unit impulse input, the Laplace transform of the resulting response can be found by putting

$$Y(s) = \mathscr{L}[\delta(t)] = 1$$

in (2.23). This yields

$$X(s) = \frac{\omega_n^2}{s^2 + 2v\omega_n s + \omega_n^2}, \quad (2.24)$$

as the Laplace transform of the impulse response, and the impulse response itself can be obtained by taking the inverse transform of the expression given in (2.24). It is necessary to distinguish between three possible types of motion depending on the value of the dimensionless damping parameter v.

(i) $+ \infty > v > 1$. In this case the characteristic equation (2.22) has two real roots given by

$$s_{1,2} = -v\omega_n \pm (v^2 - 1)^{\frac{1}{2}}\omega_n.$$

Since $\omega_n > 0$ for the present system, both these roots are negative. The impulse response transform (2.24) can be expanded in partial fractions to give

$$X(s) = \frac{\omega_n^2}{(s_1 - s_2)}\left(\frac{1}{(s - s_1)} - \frac{1}{(s - s_2)}\right).$$

It follows from entry 4 of Table 2.1 that the impulse response is

$$x(t) = \frac{\omega_n^2}{(s_1 - s_2)}(e^{s_1 t} - e^{s_2 t})$$

which, after substituting for s_1 and s_2, can be written

$$x(t) = \frac{\omega_n}{(v^2 - 1)^{\frac{1}{2}}} e^{-v\omega_n t} \sinh(v^2 - 1)^{\frac{1}{2}}\omega_n t. \qquad (2.25)$$

The impulse response is therefore non-oscillatory and tends to zero as $t \to \infty$ since $v, \omega_n > 0$.

(ii) $v = 1$. In this case the characteristic equation has two equal real roots given by

$$s_{1,2} = -\omega_n$$

which are clearly negative since $\omega_n > 0$. The impulse response transform (2.24) is now

$$X(s) = \frac{\omega_n^2}{(s + \omega_n)^2}$$

so that, according to entry 5 of Table 2.1, the impulse response is

$$x(t) = \omega_n^2 t\, e^{-\omega_n t}. \qquad (2.26)$$

This is a non-oscillatory response which tends to zero as $t \to \infty$ since $\omega_n > 0$.

(iii) $1 > v \geqslant 0$. In this case the characteristic equation has conjugate complex roots given by

$$s_{1,2} = -v\omega_n \pm i(1 - v^2)^{\frac{1}{2}}\omega_n.$$

Since $\sinh i\theta = i \sin \theta$, it may be deduced from (2.25) that the corresponding impulse response is

$$x(t) = \frac{\omega_n}{(1 - v^2)^{\frac{1}{2}}} e^{-v\omega_n t} \sin (1 - v^2)^{\frac{1}{2}}\omega_n t. \qquad (2.27)$$

This is an oscillatory response, of circular frequency $(1 - v^2)^{\frac{1}{2}}\omega_n$, whose amplitude tends to zero as $t \to \infty$ if $v > 0$. The ratio of the amplitudes a_n and a_{n+1} of any two successive cycles is a constant given by

$$\frac{a_n}{a_{n+1}} = \exp \frac{2\pi v}{(1 - v^2)^{\frac{1}{2}}}.$$

This constant is known as the *decrement* of the oscillations, and its logarithm as the *logarithmic decrement*. It is important to note that the decrement is dependent only on v and is greater than unity if $v > 0$. However, if $v = 0$, then $a_n/a_{n+1} = 1$ and equation (2.27) indicates that the impulse response is a steady oscillation given by

$$x(t) = \omega_n \sin \omega_n t.$$

This oscillation has a circular frequency ω_n, which is accordingly known as the *undamped natural frequency* of the second-order system.

The impulse response of the second-order system is plotted in Fig. 2.10 for a number of values of the dimensionless damping parameter v, and the corresponding root-loci are shown in Fig. 2.11. These loci show the trajectories of the characteristic roots in the s-plane as v increases from 0 to $+\infty$. When $v = 0$ the roots lie on the imaginary axis at $s = \pm i\omega_n$ and represent steady oscillations. When $0 < v < 1$, the conjugate complex characteristic roots lie on circular arcs of radius ω_n and represent damped oscillations with a damping parameter given by $v = \sin \theta$ (where θ is the angle between the imaginary axis and the radius vector drawn from the origin to a typical root, as indicated in Fig. 2.11). It is thus evident that the degree of damping of the oscillatory motion represented by a pair of conjugate complex roots increases with θ. Eventually, when $\theta = \pi/2$ and $v = 1$, the two characteristic roots coincide at the point $s = -\omega_n$ and the impulse response ceases to be oscillatory.† Finally, when $1 < v < +\infty$, the two roots become distinct again and lie on the negative real axis: as $v \to +\infty$, one root moves towards the origin and the other towards infinity, both roots giving rise to exponentially decaying non-oscillatory motions. Note that if v could become negative, the characteristic roots would move

† Since the transition from oscillatory to non-oscillatory behaviour occurs when $v = 1$, a second-order system for which $v = 1$ is said to be *critically damped*.

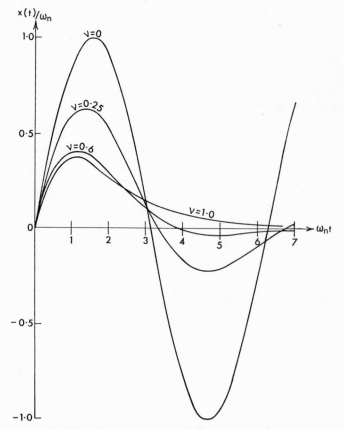

Fig. 2.10. Impulse response of second-order system.

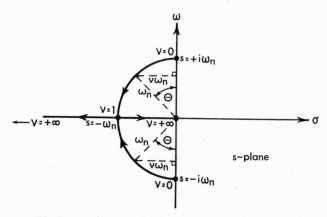

Fig. 2.11. Root-locus diagram for second-order system.

into the right half of the s-plane and all the impulse response functions given in (2.25), (2.26) and (2.27) would then tend to infinite values as $t \to \infty$.

These properties of the impulse response of the second-order system are shared by its transient response following any disturbance. Thus, if the system is set into motion by a disturbance which results in $x(0^-)$ and $x^{(1)}(0^-)$ having arbitrary non-zero values, equation (2.21) yields

$$X(s) = \frac{(s + 2v\omega_n)x(0^-) + x^{(1)}(0^-)}{s^2 + 2v\omega_n s + \omega_n^2} \qquad (2.29)$$

as the Laplace transform of the subsequent response. Since the denominator of this expression is the characteristic polynomial

$$P(s) = s^2 + 2v\omega_n s + \omega_n^2,$$

inverse transformation of (2.29) will normally yield a response function having one of the forms (2.25), (2.26) or (2.27). It should be noted, however, that it is possible for the transient response component corresponding to one of the characteristic roots to be suppressed for certain combinations of the initial conditions $x(0^-)$ and $x^{(1)}(0^-)$.†

2.4 Stability

It should now be evident that, as claimed at the end of Section 2.2, the essential properties of the possible modes of transient response of a linear system having a single response-variable $x(t)$ are determined by the nature of the roots of its characteristic equation $P(s) = 0$. It will now be shown that, as a result, the stability of such a system is also determined by these characteristic roots.

However, it is first necessary to define the concept of stability as it will be understood in the present context since many different definitions are in common use. A linear system will be said to be *stable* if the function representing its impulse response remains bounded as $t \to \infty$, and to be *unstable* otherwise: in addition, a stable system will be said to be *asymptotically stable* if its impulse response function tends to zero as $t \to \infty$. Since the transient response resulting from an arbitrary disturbance can contain only time-functions of the type which occur in the corresponding impulse response, it is a corollary of this definition that an asymptotically stable linear system will eventually return to its equilibrium position $x = 0$ after *any* disturbance. It can also be shown

† See Problem 3 at the end of this chapter for example.

that the output of a linear system which is asymptotically stable in the present sense will always remain bounded if the input is bounded. In view of these properties of asymptotic stability it is evident that an engineering system will usually be required to be asymptotically stable and not merely stable: for this reason most of the results presented in this book are criteria of asymptotic stability.

Now, for arbitrary values of the constants K_r, the components of transient response given by the expressions (2.11), (2.12), (2.13) and (2.14) will all tend to zero as $t \to \infty$ if and only if $\alpha < 0$. It follows that a linear system governed by equation (2.1) will be asymptotically stable if and only if all the real roots of the characteristic equation

$$P(s) = a_0 s^n + a_1 s^{n-1} + \ldots + a_{n-1} s + a_n = 0 \qquad (2.30)$$

are negative and all the complex roots have negative real parts. It is important to note that since $P(s)$ is the denominator of the transfer function $Q(s)/P(s)$, the characteristic roots are also the poles† of the system transfer function. An alternative statement of the last result is therefore that a system will be asymptotically stable if and only if all the real poles of its transfer function are negative and all the complex poles have negative real parts. Both the characteristic polynomial $P(s)$ and the transfer function $Q(s)/P(s)$ can of course be found simply by substituting s for D in the governing equation

$$P(D)x(t) = Q(D)y(t).$$

This correspondence between system stability and the nature of the characteristic roots (or the transfer function poles) can obviously be interpreted graphically: for it is evident that a system will be asymptotically stable if and only if all the roots of its characteristic equation lie to the left of the imaginary axis in the s-plane. This *region of asymptotic stability* is shown cross-hatched in Fig. 2.12.

It should be noted that, according to the present definition, a system having characteristic roots on the boundary of the region of asymptotic stability (i.e., on the imaginary axis) may be stable or unstable depending on the multiplicity of the roots. In fact, in the case of a system having conjugate imaginary characteristic roots $\pm i\beta$ of multiplicity p, putting $\alpha = 0$ in the expression (2.14) indicates that the corresponding impulse response component is

$$\sum_{r=1}^{p} \left[\frac{2\rho_r t^{r-1} \cos(\beta t + \psi_r)}{(r-1)!} \right]. \qquad (2.31)$$

† The *poles* of a function $H(s)$ are those finite values of s for which $H(s)$ becomes infinite. Similarly, the *zeros* of $H(s)$ are those finite values of s for which $H(s)$ vanishes.

If the roots are repeated (i.e., if $p > 1$), the last expression represents an unstable oscillation of increasing amplitude. On the other hand, if the roots are unrepeated (i.e., if $p = 1$), (2.31) reduces to

$$2\rho_1 \cos (\beta t + \psi_1)$$

which represents a steady oscillation of amplitude $2\rho_1$ and frequency β. Although this oscillation is by definition stable (since it remains bounded

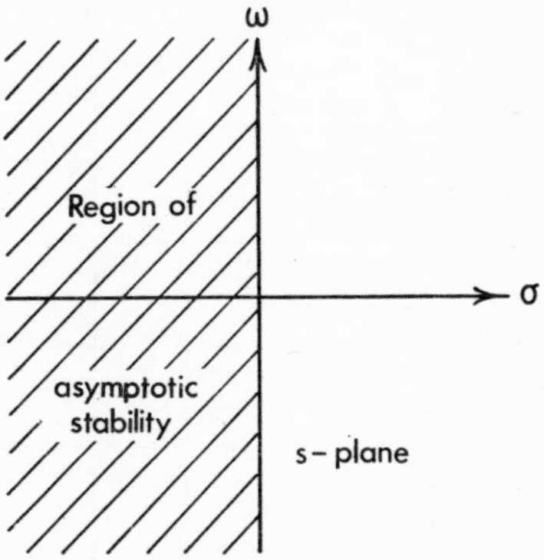

Fig. 2.12. Region of asymptotic stability in the s-plane.

as $t \to \infty$), it does not tend to zero as $t \to \infty$ and so corresponds to the boundary between stable and unstable behaviour. For this reason, a system which has no characteristic roots in the right half of the s-plane and at least one unrepeated root (but no repeated roots) on the imaginary axis is said to be *marginally stable*: such a system is evidently stable but not asymptotically stable.

The foregoing observations regarding system stability are summarised in Table 2.3. The first column of this table indicates the positions of characteristic roots in the s-plane, and the second column shows the resulting components of impulse response. In the third column these response components are classified as asymptotically stable, marginally stable or unstable. The first four entries relate to real characteristic roots and show the transition from stability to instability that occurs as a root moves along the real axis from the left to the right half-plane. The second and third entries indicate that a multiple root at the origin transforms a stable system having a bounded but non-vanishing output (i.e., a marginally stable system) into an unstable system.

The last four entries in Table 2.3 relate to pairs of conjugate complex roots and show the transition from stability to instability that occurs as the roots move into the right half-plane. The sixth and seventh entries indicate that multiple roots on the imaginary axis transform a marginally stable system into an unstable system.

TABLE 2.3

Location of characteristic roots in s-plane	Impulse response	
1		ASYMPTOTICALLY STABLE
2		MARGINALLY STABLE
3		UNSTABLE
4		UNSTABLE
5		ASYMPTOTICALLY STABLE
6		MARGINALLY STABLE
7		UNSTABLE
8		UNSTABLE

2.5 Multi-variable systems

The discussion of stability has so far been confined to simple linear systems having one input and one output variable. However, systems often have multiple input and output variables, and so, for completeness, it is necessary to demonstrate how the characteristic equations governing the stability of these more complicated systems can be derived.

In general, a linear system having q input variables $y_1(t)$, $y_2(t)$,..., $y_q(t)$, and p input variables $x_1(t)$, $x_2(t)$, ..., $x_p(t)$ is governed by a set of p simultaneous linear differential equations having the form

$$\sum_{j=1}^{p} P_{ij}(D)x_j(t) = \sum_{k=1}^{q} Q_{ik}(D)y_k(t) \ (i = 1, 2, \ldots, p), \qquad (2.32)$$

where $D \equiv d/dt$. Under the Laplace transformation this set of equations becomes

$$\sum_{j=1}^{p} P_{ij}(s)X_j(s) = \sum_{k=1}^{q} Q_{ik}(s)Y_k(s) + I_i(s) \ (i = 1, 2, \ldots, p), \qquad (2.33)$$

where the $X_j(s)$ and $Y_k(s)$ are respectively the Laplace transforms of the output and input variables. The $I_i(s)$ are polynomials in s whose coefficients are functions of the initial conditions and which vanish identically when all the initial conditions are zero.

In matrix notation, equations (2.33) can be written

$$\mathbf{P}(s)\mathbf{X}(s) = \mathbf{Q}(s)\mathbf{Y}(s) + \mathbf{I}(s),$$

where $\mathbf{P}(s)$ is the $p \times p$ square matrix† $\hspace{4cm}$ (2.34)

$$\mathbf{P}(s) = \begin{bmatrix} P_{11}(s), & P_{12}(s), & \ldots, & P_{1p}(s) \\ \cdot & \cdot & \ldots, & \cdot \\ \cdot & \cdot & \ldots, & \cdot \\ \cdot & \cdot & \ldots, & \cdot \\ P_{p1}(s), & P_{p2}(s), & \ldots, & P_{pp}(s) \end{bmatrix},$$

$\mathbf{Q}(s)$ is the $p \times q$ rectangular matrix

$$\mathbf{Q}(s) = \begin{bmatrix} Q_{11}(s), & Q_{12}(s), & \ldots, & Q_{1q}(s) \\ \cdot & \cdot & \ldots, & \cdot \\ \cdot & \cdot & \ldots, & \cdot \\ Q_{p1}(s), & Q_{p2}(s), & \ldots, & Q_{pq}(s) \end{bmatrix},$$

† In general a matrix having m rows and n columns is described as an $m \times n$ matrix.

and $\mathbf{X}(s)$, $\mathbf{Y}(s)$ and $\mathbf{I}(s)$ are vectors (i.e., column matrices) given by

$$\mathbf{X}(s) = \begin{bmatrix} X_1(s) \\ X_2(s) \\ \cdot \\ \cdot \\ \cdot \\ \cdot \\ X_p(s) \end{bmatrix}, \qquad \mathbf{Y}(s) = \begin{bmatrix} Y_1(s) \\ Y_2(s) \\ \cdot \\ \cdot \\ \cdot \\ Y_q(s) \end{bmatrix}, \qquad \mathbf{I}(s) = \begin{bmatrix} I_1(s) \\ I_2(s) \\ \cdot \\ \cdot \\ \cdot \\ I_p(s) \end{bmatrix}.$$

If $\mathbf{P}(s)$ is non-singular, equation (2.34) may be solved for the output transform vector $\mathbf{X}(s)$ to give

$$\mathbf{X}(s) = \mathbf{P}^{-1}(s)\mathbf{Q}(s)\mathbf{Y}(s) + \mathbf{P}^{-1}(s)\mathbf{I}(s), \qquad (2.35)$$

where $\mathbf{P}^{-1}(s)$ is the inverse of $\mathbf{P}(s)$. Equation (2.35) is clearly a matrix generalisation of (2.6): it is equivalent to p scalar equations which give the Laplace transforms of the p output variables in terms of the input transforms and the initial conditions.

If the system governed by equations (2.32) is initially quiescent, all the elements of the initial condition vector $\mathbf{I}(s)$ will vanish so that equation (2.35) becomes

$$\mathbf{X}(s) = \mathbf{P}^{-1}(s)\mathbf{Q}(s)\mathbf{Y}(s). \qquad (2.36)$$

The $p \times q$ matrix $\mathbf{P}^{-1}(s)\mathbf{Q}(s)$ therefore represents the input-output characteristics of the system and is accordingly known as the *transfer matrix*. Since the effect of the multi-variable system is to pre-multiply the input transform vector by the transfer matrix to produce the output transform vector, the system can be represented by the block-diagram shown in Fig. 2.13. This diagram is clearly the matrix generalisation of that shown in Fig. 2.3.

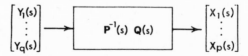

Fig. 2.13. Block diagram of system having q input and p output variables.

Now the inverse matrix $\mathbf{P}^{-1}(s)$ appearing in equation (2.36) can be expressed in the form

$$\mathbf{P}^{-1}(s) = \frac{\tilde{\mathbf{P}}(s)}{|\mathbf{P}(s)|},$$

where $|\mathbf{P}(s)|$ is the determinant of $\mathbf{P}(s)$, $\tilde{\mathbf{P}}(s)$ is the adjoint matrix of $\mathbf{P}(s)$ given by

$$\tilde{\mathbf{P}}(s) = \begin{bmatrix} \tilde{P}_{11}(s), & \tilde{P}_{12}(s), & \ldots, & \tilde{P}_{1p}(s) \\ \cdot & \cdot & \cdots, & \cdot \\ \cdot & \cdot & \cdots, & \cdot \\ \cdot & \cdot & \cdots, & \cdot \\ \tilde{P}_{p1}(s), & \tilde{P}_{p2}(s), & \ldots, & \tilde{P}_{pp}(s) \end{bmatrix},$$

and $\tilde{P}_{ij}(s)$ is the cofactor of $P_{ji}(s)$ in $|\mathbf{P}(s)|$. Equation (2.36) can therefore be written

$$X(s) = \frac{R(s)}{|\mathbf{P}(s)|}Y(s), \qquad (2.37)$$

where

$$\mathbf{R}(s) = \tilde{\mathbf{P}}(s)\mathbf{Q}(s) = \begin{bmatrix} R_{11}(s), & R_{12}(s), & \ldots, & R_{1q}(s) \\ \cdot & \cdot & \cdots, & \cdot \\ \cdot & \cdot & \cdots, & \cdot \\ \cdot & \cdot & \cdots, & \cdot \\ R_{p1}(s), & R_{p2}(s), & \ldots, & R_{pq}(s) \end{bmatrix}$$

is a $p \times q$ matrix. It follows from (2.37) that the p output transforms are given by

$$X_j(s) = \frac{1}{|\mathbf{P}(s)|}\{R_{j1}(s)Y_1(s) + R_{j2}(s)Y_2(s) + \ldots + R_{jq}(s)Y_q(s)\}$$
$$(j = 1, 2, \ldots, p). \qquad (2.38)$$

For any given set of input variables having transforms $Y_1(s)$, $Y_2(s)$, $\ldots$, $Y_q(s)$, the response of the quiescent system measured at the p output variables $x_1(t)$, $x_2(t)$, $\ldots$, $x_p(t)$ can be found by taking the inverse Laplace transforms of equations (2.38). In particular, it is evident that $x_j^{(k)}(t)$, defined as the impulse response elicited at $x_j(t)$ by unit impulse excitation applied at $y_k(t)$, is the inverse transform of the function

$$X_j^{(k)}(s) = \frac{R_{jk}(s)}{|\mathbf{P}(s)|} \ (j = 1, 2, \ldots, p; \ k = 1, 2, \ldots, q). \qquad (2.39)$$

A multi-variable system will be said to be *stable* if, for all values of j and k, these impulse response functions remain bounded as $t \to \infty$, and to be *unstable* otherwise: in addition, a stable system will be said to be *asymptotically stable* if all the impulse response functions tend to zero as $t \to \infty$. As in the case of single-variable systems, a multi-variable system which is stable but not asymptotically stable will be said to be *marginally stable*.

Now the functions $R_{jk}(s)/|\mathbf{P}(s)|$ which occur in equations (2.39) are rational algebraic functions of s of the type whose inverse transforms were studied in Section 2.2 in connection with single-variable systems. The results of the previous discussion may therefore be used in the present context. They indicate that the essential nature of the transient response of the multi-variable system is determined by the denominator of the functions given in equations (2.39). In all cases this denominator is the polynomial obtained by expanding the determinant

$$|\mathbf{P}(s)| = \begin{vmatrix} P_{11}(s), & P_{12}(s), & \ldots, & P_{1p}(s) \\ \cdot & \cdot & \cdots, & \cdot \\ \cdot & \cdot & \cdots, & \cdot \\ \cdot & \cdot & \cdots, & \cdot \\ P_{p1}(s), & P_{p2}(s), & \ldots, & P_{pp}(s) \end{vmatrix},$$

so that

$$|\mathbf{P}(s)| = 0 \qquad (2.40)$$

is the characteristic equation of the multi-variable system. This system will therefore be asymptotically stable if and only if all the roots of equation (2.40) lie in the left half of the s-plane. Note that the characteristic polynomial $|\mathbf{P}(s)|$ can be found simply by substituting s for D in the governing equations (2.32) and then forming the determinant of the functions $P_{ij}(s)$.

In the foregoing discussion, the functions defined in (2.39) were regarded as the Laplace transforms of the various impulse response functions. However, it is clear from equations (2.38) that a typical function $X_j^{(k)}(s) = R_{jk}(s)/|\mathbf{P}(s)|$ is also the transfer function relating the kth input variable $y_k(t)$ to the jth output variable $x_j(t)$. An alternative statement of the condition for the asymptotic stability of a multi-variable system is therefore that all the poles of the transfer functions $X_j^{(k)}(s)$ must lie in the left half of the s-plane.

2.6 Stability criteria

The dynamical problem of analysing the stability of a single- or multi-variable linear system has now been reduced to the algebraic problem of investigating the roots of the appropriate characteristic equation. If all the roots of this equation can be computed, it is evident that the stability of the system can be decided simply by examining the location of the characteristic roots in the s-plane. Thus, for example, the stability of a third-order system governed by the equation

$$(D^3 + 4D^2 + 9D + 10)x(t) = y(t) \qquad (2.41)$$

is determined by the values of the roots of its characteristic equation

$$s^3 + 4s^2 + 9s + 10 = 0.$$

In fact, since (as can be readily verified) these roots are equal to -2, $-1 + 2i$, $-1 - 2i$, and therefore all lie to the left of the imaginary axis in the s-plane, the system governed by equation (2.41) is asymptotically stable.

However, the scope of stability investigations which rely on the actual computation of characteristic roots is limited by the fact that it is impossible to solve an equation of any degree greater than the fourth in general algebraic terms. In such circumstances it would therefore be necessary to resort to numerical methods. Furthermore, if it were desired to make a detailed investigation of the effects of changes in parameter values on stability, it would be necessary to repeat the calculations of the characteristic roots many times. Even if a high-speed digital computer were available, this numerical approach would only rarely provide the most efficient means of investigating stability; for *stability criteria* are available which make it possible to decide the stability of a linear system without actually calculating the characteristic roots, and which can also be generalised so as to provide information regarding the *degree* of stability of stable linear systems. The following chapters of this book contain a selection of some of the most useful of these criteria.

Problems

1. Determine the characteristic equations, transfer functions, and impulse response functions of systems governed by the following differential equations, where $x(t)$ and $y(t)$ are respectively the output and input variables in each case and $D \equiv d/dt$:

(a) $(D^2 + 4D + 3)x(t) = y(t)$.
(b) $(D^2 - 4D + 3)x(t) = y(t)$.
(c) $(D^2 + 4D + 4)x(t) = y(t)$.
(d) $(D^2 + D + 4)x(t) = y(t)$.
(e) $(D^2 - D + 1)x(t) = y(t)$.
(f) $(D^2 + 4)(D + 1)x(t) = (D + 2)y(t)$.
(g) $(D^2 + 4)^2(D + 1)x(t) = (D + 2)y(t)$.
(h) $(D^2 + 4)^2(D - 1)x(t) = (D + 2)y(t)$.
(i) $(D + 2)(D + 3)(D - 1)x(t) = y(t)$.

Classify each system as asymptotically stable, marginally stable or unstable, and plot each set of characteristic roots in the s-plane.

2. Prove that if the Laplace transforms of two function $f_1(t)$ and $f_2(t)$ are $F_1(s)$ and $F_2(s)$, respectively, then

$$\mathscr{L}^{-1}[F_1(s)F_2(s)] = \int_0^\infty f_1(t - \tau)f_2(\tau)d\tau$$

if $f_1(t) = 0 = f_2(t)$ when $t < 0$. Hence show that the response of an initially quiescent single-variable linear system to an arbitrary input $y(t)$, applied at $t = 0$, is given by

$$x(t) = \int_0^\infty g(t - \tau)y(\tau)d\tau = \int_0^\infty g(\tau)y(t - \tau)d\tau,$$

where $g(t)$ is response of the system to a unit impulse applied at $t = 0$. Use this result to show that the response of an asymptotically stable linear system to a bounded input is a bounded function of time.

3. Determine the impulse response of a system governed by the equation

$$(D^2 + 2D - 3)x(t) = y(t) \quad (D \equiv d/dt),$$

and thus show that the system is unstable. Determine also the transient response of the system if $x(0^-) = 1$, $x^{(1)}(0^-) = -3$, and $y(t) = 0$, and show that the function representing this response vanishes as $t \to \infty$. Comment on the significance of this result.

4. Determine the characteristic equations, transfer matrices, and impulse response functions of multi-variable systems governed by the following sets of differential equations, where the $x_j(t)$ and $y_k(t)$ are respectively the output and input variables in each case and $D \equiv d/dt$:

(a) $(D + 2)x_1(t) + (D + 1)x_2(t) = y_1(t)$,
$x_1(t) + (D + 1)x_2 = y_2(t)$.

(b) $(D^2 + 2)x_1(t) + 3x_2(t) = y_1(t)$,
$3x_1(t) + (D + 4)x_2(t) = y_2(t)$.

(c) $(D + 1)x_1(t) + 4x_2(t) = (D - 1)y_1(t)$,
$2x_1(t) + (D + 3)x_2(t) = y_2(t)$.

Classify each system as asymptotically stable, marginally stable or unstable, and plot each set of characteristic roots in the s-plane.

Chapter 3

ENCIRCLEMENT THEOREM: CRITERIA OF LEONHARD AND NYQUIST

3.1 Encirclement theorem

Many of the stability criteria to be presented in this book can be derived from a theorem in complex-variable theory known as the encirclement theorem. In this chapter the encirclement theorem is proved for rational algebraic functions of a complex variable and is then used to obtain the criteria of Leonhard and of Nyquist. In the next chapter the theorem is used to derive Routh's stability criterion which in turn leads to the alternative criterion of Hurwitz given in Chapter 5. The encirclement theorem is also used in Chapter 8 to investigate the stability of systems governed by differential-difference equations.

Now a rational algebraic function of the complex variable s, having zeros at $s = z_1, z_2, \ldots, z_m$ and poles at $s = p_1, p_2, \ldots, p_n$, can be written in the factored form

$$H(s) = \lambda \frac{(s - z_1)(s - z_2) \ldots (s - z_m)}{(s - p_1)(s - p_2) \ldots (s - p_n)}, \tag{3.1}$$

where λ is a constant. It is evident that if a value is assigned to $s = \sigma + i\omega$, $H(s)$ will itself be a complex number of the form

$$H(s) = U(\sigma, \omega) + iV(\sigma, \omega).$$

In geometrical terms, this means that to any point (σ, ω) in the s-plane there corresponds a point (U, V) in the $H(s)$-plane. It follows that if the point (σ, ω) traverses a contour C in the s-plane, the point (U, V) will describe a corresponding contour Γ in the $H(s)$-plane (Fig. 3.1).

Now consider any simple† closed contour C such as that shown in Fig. 3.1(a). If C is traversed once in the clockwise sense, the change in the argument of the complex number represented by the point (U, V) in the $H(s)$-plane will be given by

$$\Delta \arg H(s) = \sum_{r=1}^{m} \Delta \arg (s - z_r) - \sum_{r=1}^{n} \Delta \arg (s - p_r) \tag{3.2}$$

† Note that a contour is *simple* if it does not intersect itself.

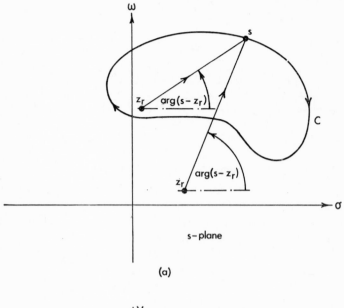

(a)

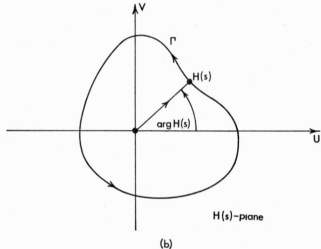

(b)

Fig. 3.1. Corresponding contours in the s-plane and the $H(s)$-plane.

since it is evident from equation (3.1) that

$$\arg H(s) = \sum_{r=1}^{m} \arg (s - z_r) - \sum_{r=1}^{n} \arg (s - p_r).$$

The first summation term in the right-hand member of equation (3.2) can be evaluated by noting that arg $(s - z_r)$ is the argument of the complex number represented by the vector drawn from the zero z_r to a point s on the contour C, and that $\Delta \arg (s - z_r)$ is the change in this angle as C is traversed once in the clockwise sense. It follows that $\Delta \arg (s - z_r)$ is equal to -2π or 0 according as the zero z_r is inside or outside C (see Fig. 3.1(a)). Hence, if Z zeros of $H(s)$ lie within C, it may be inferred that

$$\sum_{r=1}^{m} \Delta \arg (s - z_r) = -2\pi Z.$$

Similarly, if P poles of $H(s)$ lie within C, it is evident that

$$\sum_{r=1}^{n} \Delta \arg (s - p_r) = -2\pi P.$$

It may therefore be deduced from equation (3.2) that

$$\Delta \arg H(s) = 2\pi(P - Z), \tag{3.3}$$

i.e., that

$$N = P - Z, \tag{3.4}$$

where $N = \Delta \arg H(s)/2\pi$. Since N is clearly the number of times the origin in the $H(s)$-plane is encircled in the anti-clockwise sense as the contour C is traversed once in the clockwise sense, the result expressed by equation (3.4) or (3.3) is called the *encirclement theorem*. It is important to note that this theorem is valid only if no poles or zeros of $H(s)$ lie on the contour C. Also, provided the last condition is satisfied, the validity of the theorem is not restricted to rational algebraic functions.

3.2 Application to characteristic polynomials: Leonhard's criterion

If

$$F(s) = a_0 s^n + a_1 s^{n-1} + \ldots + a_{n-1} s + a_n = 0 \tag{3.5}$$

is the characteristic equation of a single- or multi-variable linear system, it was shown in Chapter 2 that the system will be asymptotically stable if and only if all the characteristic roots lie in the left half of the s-plane. The encirclement theorem can be used to ascertain whether or not this is the case by choosing as the contour C the special contour C^* shown in Fig. 3.2. This contour is known as the *stability contour* and consists of the whole of the imaginary axis between $\omega = -\infty$ and $\omega = +\infty$, together with the infinite semi-circular arc which encompasses the entire right half of the s-plane.

Now the characteristic polynomial $F(s)$ has no poles of any type and therefore certainly no poles lying within the contour C^*. Consequently,

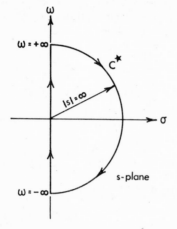

Fig. 3.2. Stability contour C^*.

if $F(s)$ has k zeros with positive real parts and no imaginary zeros,† the encirclement theorem (3.3) indicates that

$$\Delta \arg F(s) = -2k\pi, \tag{3.6}$$

where $\Delta \arg F(s)$ is the change in the argument of $F(s)$ as the stability contour C^* is traversed once in the clockwise sense.

Equation (3.6) can be expressed in a form which is more convenient for the calculation of k by considering the separate contributions made to $\Delta \arg F(s)$ by the straight and semi-circular parts of C^*. Thus, on the semi-circular part of C^*,

$$s = re^{i\theta},$$

where θ decreases from $+\pi/2$ to $-\pi/2$ and r is infinite. Since $a_0 s^n$ becomes the dominant term in $F(s)$ as $|s| \to \infty$, it is evident that $F(s)$ is effectively equal to

$$a_0 r^n e^{in\theta}$$

when s lies on the infinite semi-circle. It follows that $\arg F(s)$ will decrease from $+n\pi/2$ to $-n\pi/2$ as θ decreases from $+\pi/2$ to $-\pi/2$, and therefore that

$$\Delta \arg F(s) = -n\pi \tag{3.7}$$

† This restriction is essential since the encirclement theorem is valid only if no poles or zeros lie on the contour in the s-plane.

on the semi-circular part of C^*. Thus, if

$$\arg F(i\omega) = \Phi(\omega)$$

and $[\Delta\Phi]_{-\infty}^{+\infty}$ is the change in $\arg F(s)$ as ω increases from $-\infty$ to $+\infty$ along the imaginary axis $s = i\omega$ ($-\infty < \omega < +\infty$), equations (3.6) and (3.7) may be combined to give

$$[\Delta\Phi]_{-\infty}^{+\infty} = (n - 2k)\pi. \tag{3.8}$$

The number of roots of equation (3.5) having positive real parts is therefore

$$k = \frac{1}{2}\left\{n - \frac{1}{\pi}[\Delta\Phi]_{-\infty}^{+\infty}\right\}. \tag{3.9}$$

The last result obviously reduces the problem of calculating k to that of determining the angle $[\Delta\Phi]_{-\infty}^{+\infty}$ for any given characteristic polynomial. Consider, for example, the characteristic equation

$$F(s) = s^4 + s^3 + s^2 + 2s + 3 = 0 \tag{3.10}$$

for which

$$F(i\omega) = (\omega^4 - \omega^2 + 3) + i(-\omega^3 + 2\omega)$$

and

$$\Phi(\omega) = \arg F(i\omega) = \tan^{-1}\left(\frac{-\omega^3 + 2\omega}{\omega^4 - \omega^2 + 3}\right).$$

The locus of $F(i\omega)$ as ω increases from $-\infty$ to $+\infty$ has the form shown in Fig. 3.3. It is evident that $\Phi(-\infty) = 0 = \Phi(+\infty)$ and also that $[\Delta\Phi]_{-\infty}^{+\infty} = 0$. It is also apparent that the $F(i\omega)$-locus does not pass through the origin, thus indicating that equation (3.10) has no imaginary roots and therefore that equation (3.9) is applicable. In fact, since $n = 4$ in the case of equation (3.10), it may be concluded from (3.9) that $k = 2$, i.e., equation (3.10) has two roots with positive real parts and so represents an unstable system. It should be noted that, since equation (3.10) has real coefficients, the $F(i\omega)$-locus is symmetrical about the real axis (i.e., the sections of the locus corresponding to positive and negative values of ω are mirror images of each other).

Now, to revert to the general case, a system governed by an equation of the form (3.5) will be asymptotically stable if and only if no characteristic roots lie in the right half of the s-plane (i.e., $k = 0$) and no roots lie on the imaginary axis. It may therefore be deduced from equation (3.8) that, if the appropriate $F(i\omega)$-locus does not pass through the origin, it is necessary and sufficient for asymptotic stability that

$$[\Delta\Phi]_{-\infty}^{+\infty} = n\pi, \tag{3.11}$$

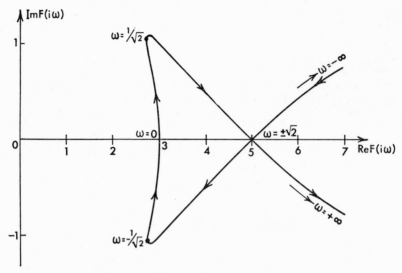

Fig. 3.3. $F(i\omega)$-locus for equation 3.10.

i.e., a system governed by an nth degree characteristic equation with no imaginary roots† will be asymptotically stable if and only if arg $F(i\omega)$ increases by $n\pi$ when ω increases from $-\infty$ to $+\infty$.

This statement of the stability criterion applies equally to real or complex characteristic equations. However, if the coefficients in the characteristic equation are real, equation (3.11) can be simplified in view of the resulting symmetry of the $F(i\omega)$-locus. In fact, it is then only necessary to consider the $F(i\omega)$-locus for positive values of ω since then

$$[\Delta\Phi]_{-\infty}^{+\infty} = 2[\Delta\Phi]_{0}^{+\infty}.$$

It may therefore be deduced from (3.11) that, in the case of a real nth degree characteristic equation with no imaginary roots, it is necessary and sufficient for asymptotic stability that

$$[\Delta\Phi]_{0}^{+\infty} = \frac{n\pi}{2}. \tag{3.12}$$

If equation (3.5) is arranged so that $a_n > 0$, the last statement of the criterion implies that a real nth degree characteristic equation repre-

† Although a system having a characteristic equation with imaginary roots cannot be asymptotically stable, it can still be marginally stable if the imaginary roots are unrepeated: it is possible to use the encirclement theorem to derive a criterion of marginal stability in such cases by deforming the stability contour so as to exclude the imaginary characteristic roots (see Problem 6 at the end of this chapter).

sents an asymptotically stable system if and only if $\Phi(\omega)$ increases continuously from 0 to $n\pi/2$ as increases from 0 to $+\infty$. This in turn implies that if

$$F(i\omega) = P(\omega) + iQ(\omega), \tag{3.13}$$

then all the zeros of $P(\omega)$ and $Q(\omega)$ must be real, simple and alternating to ensure asymptotic stability. In other words, if the positive zeros of $P(\omega)$ and $Q(\omega)$ are $\omega_1, \omega_2, \omega_3, \ldots$, and $\omega_\mathrm{I}, \omega_\mathrm{II}, \omega_\mathrm{III}, \ldots$, respectively, it is necessary and sufficient for asymptotic stability that

$$\omega_\mathrm{I} < \omega_1 < \omega_\mathrm{II} < \omega_2 < \omega_\mathrm{III} < \omega_3 \ldots,$$

and also that $P(\omega)$ and $Q(\omega)$ have no complex or repeated zeros. It should be evident from Fig. 3.4 that only in such circumstances will the

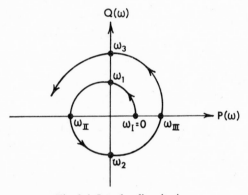

Fig. 3.4. Leonhard's criterion.

condition (3.12) be satisfied. In this form, the stability criterion is known as *Leonhard's criterion*[†] (in the Soviet literature it is known as *Mikhailov's criterion*[‡]).

The use of Leonhard's criterion can be illustrated by considering the real characteristic equation

$$F(s) = s^5 + s^4 + 20s^3 + 10s^2 + 64s + 9 = 0. \tag{3.14}$$

In this case,

$$F(i\omega) = (\omega^4 - 10\omega^2 + 9) + i(\omega^5 - 20\omega^3 + 64\omega)$$

[†] A. Leonhard, Neues Verfahren zur Stabilitatsuntesuchung, *Arch. Elektrotech.*, **38**, 17, 1944.
[‡] A. Mikhailov, Metod garmonicheskovo analiza v teorii regulirovanija, *Automatika Telemek.*, **3**, 27, 1938.

so that, in the notation of equation (3.13),

$$P(\omega) = \omega^4 - 10\omega^2 + 9 \equiv (\omega^2 - 1)(\omega^2 - 9)$$

and

$$Q(\omega) = \omega^5 - 20\omega^3 + 64\omega \equiv \omega(\omega^2 - 4)(\omega^2 - 16).$$

The zeros of $P(\omega)$ and $Q(\omega)$ are obviously all real and simple. Furthermore, the positive zeros of $P(\omega)$ are $\omega_1 = 1$, $\omega_2 = 3$, and those of $Q(\omega)$ are $\omega_I = 0$, $\omega_{II} = 2$, $\omega_{III} = 4$. Since these two sets of zeros

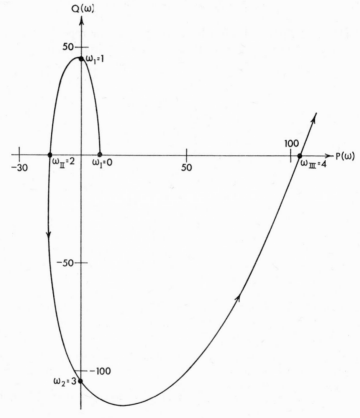

Fig. 3.5. Application of Leonhard's criterion to equation 3.14.

alternate, it follows from Leonhard's criterion that equation (3.14) represents an asymptotically stable system. This conclusion is confirmed by the plot of $F(i\omega)$ shown in Fig. 3.5 which indicates that the condition (3.12) is satisfied.

3.3 Application to transfer functions

It was pointed out in Chapter 2 that the characteristic polynomial of a linear system is the denominator of the transfer function relating any pair of input and output variables, and consequently that a system will be asymptotically stable if and only if all the poles of these transfer functions have negative real parts. It follows that system stability can be determined by investigating the poles of transfer functions rather than the zeros of characteristic polynomials. This alternative approach is often the more convenient, particularly when the dynamical characteristics of a system are known only in terms of experimentally determined harmonic response characteristics.

The location in the s-plane of the poles of a transfer function $T(s)$ can be investigated by using the encirclement theorem and the stability contour C^* (Fig. 3.2). In fact, if the transfer function has k poles and h zeros with positive real parts, and no imaginary poles or zeros, it follows from (3.3) that

$$\Delta \arg T(s) = 2\pi(k - h), \tag{3.15}$$

where $\Delta \arg T(s)$ is the change in the argument of $T(s)$ as C^* is traversed once in the clockwise sense.

In practical systems, the numerator of $T(s)$ is usually not of higher degree than the denominator. In such circumstances it is evident that $T(s)$ will be equal to a constant (possibly zero) when s lies on the infinite semi-circular part of C^*, and therefore that this part of C^* will make no contribution to $\Delta \arg T(s)$. If $\arg T(i\omega) = \Psi(\omega)$, it may therefore be concluded from equation (3.15) that the change in $\Psi(\omega)$ as ω increases from $-\infty$ to $+\infty$ will then be given by

$$[\Delta\Psi]_{-\infty}^{+\infty} = 2\pi(k - h) \tag{3.16}$$

and consequently that

$$k = h + \frac{1}{2\pi}[\Delta\Psi]_{-\infty}^{+\infty}. \tag{3.17}$$

Now h can usually be found by inspection, and $[\Delta\Psi]_{-\infty}^{+\infty}$ can be found by plotting the locus of $T(i\omega)$ as ω increases from $-\infty$ to $+\infty$.† Thus, k (i.e., the number of poles having positive real parts) can be deduced from equation (3.17). Since, if there are no imaginary poles,

---

† This locus determines the harmonic response characteristics of an asymptotically stable linear system having a transfer function $T(s)$; for it can be shown (see Section 3.5) that the steady-state response of such a system to an input $a \sin \omega t$ is given by $|T(i\omega)|a \sin \{\omega t + \arg T(i\omega)\}$.

it is necessary and sufficient for asymptotic stability that $k = 0$, the corresponding stability criterion in terms of $\Psi(\omega)$ is clearly that

$$[\Delta\Psi]^{+\infty}_{-\infty} = -2\pi h. \tag{3.18}$$

These results can be illustrated by investigating the stability of a system having a transfer function

$$T(s) = \frac{s - 1}{s^3 + s^2 + s + 3}. \tag{3.19}$$

The locus of $T(i\omega)$ as ω increases from $-\infty$ to $+\infty$ is shown in Fig. 3.6. Since this locus passes through the origin when $\omega = \pm\infty$, it is

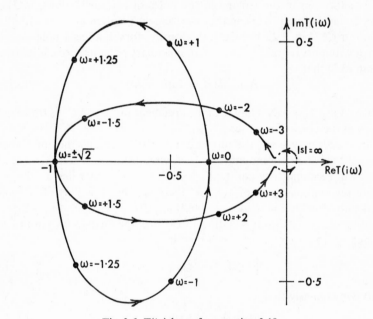

Fig. 3.6. $T(i\omega)$-locus for equation 3.19.

necessary to consider that those parts of C^* where $|s| = \infty$ are approached by a limiting process. This reveals that the $T(i\omega)$-locus approaches the origin from the right as $|s| \to \infty$, and consequently that the origin is encircled once in the anti-clockwise sense. Hence, $[\Delta\Psi]^{+\infty}_{-\infty} = 2\pi$. Since $h = 1$ (the transfer function (3.19) has one zero inside C^* at $s = +1$), it may be deduced from equation (3.17) that $k = 2$. This means that two poles of the transfer function have positive real parts and consequently that the system governed by (3.19) is unstable.

3.4 Closed-loop control systems: Nyquist's criterion

The block-diagram of any closed-loop system incorporating negative feedback and having one input and one output variable can be reduced to the form shown in Fig. 3.7.† The input and output variables have Laplace transforms $X_i(s)$ and $X_0(s)$, respectively, and the forward path of the system has a transfer function $G(s)$. This function is known as the *open-loop transfer function* since it describes the behaviour of the system when the feedback loop is open.

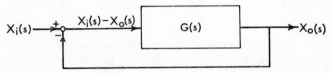

Fig. 3.7. Block diagram of a closed-loop system having unity feedback and one input and one output variable.

However, when the loop is closed, the input to $G(s)$ is the error signal $x_i(t) - x_0(t)$ which clearly has a Laplace transform $X_i(s) - X_0(s)$. Hence, if the system is initially quiescent, it follows that

$$X_0(s) = G(s)[X_i(s) - X_0(s)]$$

and therefore that

$$\frac{X_o(s)}{X_i(s)} = \frac{G(s)}{1 + G(s)}. \tag{3.20}$$

This equation determines the overall behaviour of the system when the loop is closed, and $G(s)/[1 + G(s)]$ is accordingly known as the *closed-loop transfer function*. The general considerations of Section 2.4 indicate that the stability of the closed-loop system is governed by the poles of this function, i.e., by the zeros of its denominator $[1 + G(s)]$. In particular, it is evident that the closed-loop system will be asymptotically stable if and only if all the roots of the characteristic equation

$$1 + G(s) = 0 \tag{3.21}$$

have negative real parts.

The location of these characteristic roots in the s-plane can be investigated by means of the encirclement theorem (3.3). Thus, if $[1 + G(s)]$ has no imaginary poles or zeros, and if the numerator of $G(s)$ is not of higher degree than the denominator, application of equa-

† A closed-loop system with a block-diagram of this form is said to have *unity feedback* since the transfer function of the feedback path is unity.

tion (3.3) to the function $[1 + G(s)]$ and the stability contour C^* yields an equation of the form

$$[\Delta\Psi]^{+\infty}_{-\infty} = 2\pi(h - k), \qquad (3.22)$$

where h and k are respectively the numbers of poles and zeros of $[1 + G(s)]$ having positive real parts, and $[\Delta\Psi]^{+\infty}_{-\infty}/2\pi$ is the number of anti-clockwise encirclements of the origin by the $[1 + G(i\omega)]$-locus as ω increases from $-\infty$ to $+\infty$. Since, if there are no imaginary characteristic zeros, it is necessary and sufficient for asymptotic stability that $k = 0$, equation (3.22) implies that the closed-loop system will be asymptotically stable if and only if

$$[\Delta\Psi]^{+\infty}_{-\infty} = 2\pi h \qquad (3.23a)$$

and the $[1 + G(i\omega)]$-locus does not pass through the origin.†

This criterion of closed-loop stability can be given a different interpretation by invoking the simple relationship that exists between the function $[1 + G(s)]$ and the open-loop transfer function $G(s)$: for it is evident that $[1 + G(s)]$ and $G(s)$ have the same poles (i.e., these functions become infinite for the same values of s), and also that the origin in the $[1 + G(s)]$-plane corresponds to the point $(-1, 0)$ in the $G(s)$-plane. It follows that, in equation (3.23a), h can be interpreted as the number of poles of $G(s)$ having positive real parts, and $[\Delta\Psi]^{+\infty}_{-\infty}/2\pi$ as the number of anti-clockwise encirclements of the point $(-1, 0)$ by the $G(i\omega)$-locus as ω increases from $-\infty$ to $+\infty$. It is therefore necessary and sufficient for the asymptotic stability of the closed-loop system that equation (3.23a) (with this new interpretation) is satisfied, and that the $G(i\omega)$-locus does not pass through $(-1, 0)$.† In this form, the result is known as *Nyquist's criterion*.‡

The great importance of Nyquist's criterion lies in the fact that it makes it possible to decide the stability of a *closed*-loop system on the basis of the values of $[\Delta\Psi]^{+\infty}_{-\infty}$ and h, which are properties of the appropriate *open*-loop transfer function $G(s)$. It is usually possible to find h by inspection, and the angle $[\Delta\Psi]^{+\infty}_{-\infty}$ can be found from the $G(i\omega)$-locus. This locus can be obtained by evaluating $G(s)$ for imaginary arguments if the open-loop transfer function is known analytically: alternatively, the locus can be found experimentally from open-loop harmonic response tests (see Section 3.5). Note that if the open-loop system is itself stable, then $G(s)$ has no poles with positive real parts and equation (3.23a) becomes

$$[\Delta\Psi]^{+\infty}_{-\infty} = 0. \qquad (3.23b)$$

† It is evident that if $s = i\Omega$ is an imaginary closed-loop characteristic zero, then $1 + G(i\Omega) = 0$ and $G(i\Omega) = -1$.

‡ H. Nyquist, Regeneration Theory, *Bell System Tech. J.*, **11**, 126, 1932.

As a first illustration of the use of Nyquist's criterion consider the simple closed-loop control system whose block-diagram is shown in Fig. 3.8(a). In this case, the open-loop transfer function is

$$G(s) = \frac{10}{0 \cdot 5s + 1}$$

which has a pole at $s = -2$. However, this pole does not lie within the stability contour C^* and so $h = 0$ in equation (3.22). Also, it is evident

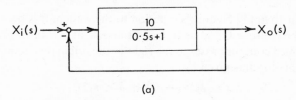

(a)

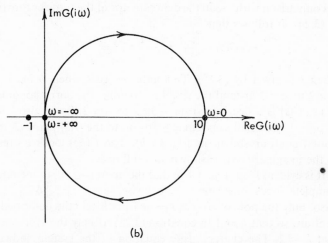

(b)

Fig. 3.8. Application of Nyquist's criterion to a first-order system.

from Fig. 3.8(b) that the $G(i\omega)$-locus does not pass through or enclose the point $(-1, 0)$ so that there are no imaginary characteristic roots and $[\Delta\Psi]_{-\infty}^{+\infty} = 0$. It may therefore be deduced from (3.22) that $k = 0$, i.e., the closed-loop system is asymptotically stable. This result can easily be checked by noting that in this case the characteristic equation $[1 + G(s)] = 0$ is

$$0 \cdot 5s + 11 = 0$$

whose root ($s_1 = -22$) obviously lies in the left-hand of the s-plane.

If any poles of an open-loop transfer function lie on the imaginary axis, it is necessary to use a slightly modified version of the stability contour C^*. This technique can be explained by considering the closed-loop system whose block-diagram is shown in Fig. 3.9(a). The open-loop transfer function in this case is

$$G(s) = \frac{1}{s(s-1)} \tag{3.24}$$

which has poles at $s = 0$ and $s = +1$, the former lying on the imaginary axis.

In order to apply Nyquist's criterion to this system it is necessary to deform the contour C^* so as to avoid the pole at $s = 0$. In Fig. 3.9(b) the deformed contour passes to the right of the origin on a semi-circular path of small radius given by

$$s = \rho e^{i\phi} \; (-\pi/2 < \phi < \pi/2), \tag{3.25}$$

where ρ is the radius. Now when $\rho = |s|$ is small, s^2 may be neglected in comparison with $-s$ in the denominator of the transfer function given in (3.24). It follows that

$$G(s) \simeq -\frac{1}{s} = -\frac{1}{\rho} e^{-i\phi} = \frac{1}{\rho} e^{i(\pi-\phi)}$$

when s is given by (3.25). This indicates that when ϕ increases from $-\pi/2$ to $+\pi/2$ around the small semi-circle, the corresponding change in arg $G(s)$ is a decrease from $+3\pi/2$ to $+\pi/2$. Since also $|G(s)| \to \infty$ as $\rho \to 0$, the small semi-circle maps on to the $G(s)$-plane as the chain-dotted contour shown in Fig. 3.9(b). The $G(i\omega)$-locus corresponding to the imaginary axis is shown as a full line.

It is evident from Fig. 3.9(b) that the point $(-1, 0)$ is encircled by the complete locus once in the clockwise sense, i.e., $[\Delta\Psi]_{-\infty}^{+\infty} = -2\pi$. Also, only the pole of $G(s)$ at $s = +1$ lies inside the deformed stability contour, so that $h = 1$ in equation (3.22). It may therefore be deduced that $k = 2$. The characteristic equation of the system shown in Fig. 3.9(a) consequently has two roots with positive real parts and is therefore unstable. This result can be checked by noting that in this case the characteristic equation $[1 + G(s)] = 0$ is

$$s^2 - s + 1 = 0$$

whose two roots are $s_{1,2} = \dfrac{1}{2} \pm i\dfrac{\sqrt{3}}{2}$.

It is important to note that the same result can be obtained by de-forming the stability contour so that it passes to the left of the origin, as shown in Fig. 3.9(c). In this case, the small semi-circle is given by

$$s = \rho e^{i\phi} \; (+\pi/2 < \phi < +3\pi/2).$$

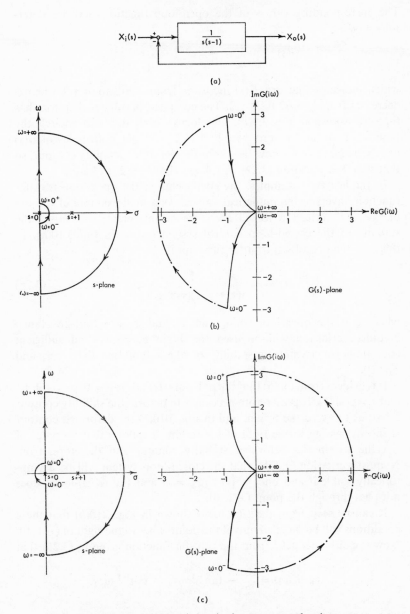

Fig. 3.9. Application of Nyquist's criterion to a second-order system.

The corresponding values of the open-loop function $G(s)$ are determined by

$$G(s) \simeq -\frac{1}{s} = -\frac{1}{\rho} e^{-i\phi} = \frac{1}{\rho} e^{i(\pi - \phi)}$$

which indicates that arg $G(s)$ increases from $-\pi/2$ to $+\pi/2$ when ϕ decreases from $+3\pi/2$ to $+\pi/2$. The complete $G(s)$-locus therefore has the form shown in Fig. 3.9(c). This locus clearly does not encircle the point $(-1, 0)$, i.e., in this case $[\Delta\Psi]_{-\infty}^{+\infty} = 0$. But both poles of $G(s)$ at $s = 0$ and $s = +1$ now lie within the deformed stability contour, so that $h = 2$ in equation (3.22). It follows that $k = 2$, as before.

In the last two examples, the coefficients in the open-loop transfer function have specific numerical values. As a final example of the use of Nyquist's criterion it will therefore be instructive to analyse the stability of the closed-loop control system shown in Fig. 3.10(a). In this case the open-loop transfer function is

$$G(s) = \frac{\xi}{s(\tau_1 s + 1)(\tau_2 s + 1)}, \tag{3.26}$$

where ξ is the open-loop gain, and τ_1 and τ_2 are time-constants. Nyquist's criterion will be used to obtain necessary and sufficient conditions for asymptotic stability on the assumption that ξ, τ_1 and $\tau_2 > 0$.

It is evident from (3.26) that the poles of $G(s)$ are at $s = 0, s = -1/\tau_1$, and $s = -1/\tau_2$. It is therefore necessary to deform the stability contour C^* so as to avoid the origin, and in Fig. 3.10(b) the deformed contour is shown passing to the right of the origin. It follows that no poles of $G(s)$ lie within the deformed stability contour and therefore, from Nyquist's criterion (3.23b), that the closed-loop system will be asymptotically stable if and only if $[\Delta\Psi]_{-\infty}^{+\infty} = 0$ and the $G(i\omega)$-locus does not pass through the point $(-1, 0)$.

It can be seen from the $G(s)$-locus shown in Fig. 3.10(b) that these conditions will be satisfied only if the point A lies to the right of $(-1, 0)$. Now it can be deduced from the transfer function given in (3.26) that

$$\arg G(i\omega) = \frac{3\pi}{2} - \tan^{-1} \omega\tau_1 - \tan^{-1} \omega\tau_2.$$

Also, it is evident from Fig. 3.10(b) that arg $G(i\omega) = \pi$ at A. Hence,

$$\frac{3\pi}{2} - \tan^{-1} \omega\tau_1 - \tan^{-1} \omega\tau_2 = \pi$$

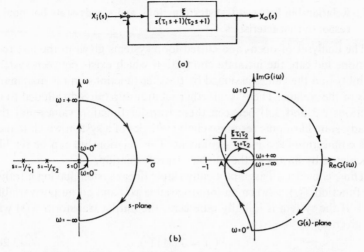

Fig. 3.10. Application to Nyquist's criterion to a third-order system.

giving

$$\tan^{-1}\frac{\omega(\tau_1 + \tau_2)}{1 - \omega^2\tau_1\tau_2} = \frac{\pi}{2}$$

and consequently

$$\omega^2 = \frac{1}{\tau_1\tau_2} \tag{3.27}$$

at A.

The distance of A from the origin can now be found by substituting from (3.27) into the expression

$$|G(i\omega)| = \frac{\xi}{\omega(\omega^2\tau_1^2 + 1)^{\frac{1}{2}}(\omega^2\tau_2^2 + 1)^{\frac{1}{2}}}.$$

This gives

$$|G(i\omega)| = \frac{\xi\tau_1\tau_2}{\tau_1 + \tau_2}$$

at A. The $G(s)$-locus will therefore not enclose or pass through the point $(-1, 0)$ if and only if

$$\frac{\xi\tau_1\tau_2}{\tau_1 + \tau_2} < 1,$$

which is accordingly the condition for the asymptotic stability of the closed-loop system shown in Fig. 3.10(a).

3.5 Relationship between transfer functions and steady-state harmonic-response characteristics

The analyses of open- and closed-loop systems given in the last two sections indicate the intimate connection which exists between system stability and the values assumed by transfer functions on the imaginary axis of the s-plane. There is a further relationship (already alluded to in Sections 3.3 and 3.4) between these transfer function values and the steady-state harmonic response characteristics of a system which makes this connection even more significant. This relationship can be readily elucidated by means of the Laplace transformation.

Thus, consider an asymptotically stable linear system having a transfer function $T(s)$ between an input variable $y(t)$ and an output variable $x(t)$. If the system is initially quiescent, the output transform $X(s)$ will be given by

$$X(s) = T(s) Y(s), \tag{3.28}$$

where $Y(s)$ is the input transform. In the particular case of a harmonic input $y(t) = a \sin \omega t$, the input transform is

$$Y(s) = \frac{a\omega}{s^2 + \omega^2} = \frac{a\omega}{(s - i\omega)(s + i\omega)}$$

and eqation (3.28) becomes

$$X(s) = T(s)\frac{a\omega}{(s - i\omega)(s + i\omega)}. \tag{3.29}$$

If the characteristic zeros of the system (i.e., the poles of $T(s)$) are s_j ($j = 1, 2, \ldots, r$), where s_j has multiplicity p_j, then the output transform given in equation (3.29) will have a partial fraction expansion of the form

$$X(s) = \frac{c_1}{(s - i\omega)} + \frac{c_2}{(s + i\omega)} + \sum_{j=1}^{r} \left\{ \sum_{k=1}^{p_j} \frac{L_{jk}}{(s - s_j)^k} \right\}, \tag{3.30}$$

where the L_{jk} are real or complex constants and

$$\begin{aligned}
c_1 &= [(s - i\omega)X(s)]_{s=i\omega} = \frac{a}{2i}T(i\omega), \\
c_2 &= [(s + i\omega)X(s)]_{s=-i\omega} = -\frac{a}{2i}T(-i\omega).
\end{aligned}$$

Inverse transformation of equation (3.30) indicates that the output is given by

$$x(t) = \frac{a}{2i}T(i\omega)\,e^{i\omega t} - \frac{a}{2i}T(-i\omega)\,e^{-i\omega t} \qquad (3.31)$$

$$+ \sum_{j=1}^{r} \left\{ \sum_{k=1}^{p_j} \frac{L_{jk}t^{k-1}}{(k-1)!} \right\} e^{s_j t}.$$

Since the system is asymptotically stable, all the s_j $(j = 1, 2, \ldots, r)$ have negative real parts and consequently

$$\lim_{t \to \infty} \sum_{j=1}^{r} \left\{ \sum_{k=1}^{p_j} \frac{L_{jk}t^{k-1}}{(k-1)!} \right\} e^{s_j t} = 0.$$

It therefore follows from equation (3.31) that the steady-state harmonic response of the system (i.e., the response when $t \to \infty$) is given by

$$x_{ss}(t) = \frac{a}{2i}T(i\omega)\,e^{i\omega t} - \frac{a}{2i}T(-i\omega)\,e^{-i\omega t}.$$

Now if the system has real parameters, then

$$|T(-i\omega)| = |T(i\omega)|$$

and

$$\arg T(-i\omega) = -\arg T(i\omega).$$

Hence,

$$x_{ss}(t) = \frac{a}{2i}|T(i\omega)|[\exp i\{\omega t + \arg T(i\omega)\}$$

$$- \exp -i\{\omega t + \arg T(i\omega)\}]$$

$$= |T(i\omega)|a \sin \{\omega t + \arg T(i\omega)\} \qquad (3.32)$$

in such cases.

Equation (3.32) indicates that if an asymptotically stable linear system having a transfer function $T(s)$ is subjected to a sinusoidal input of amplitude a and frequency ω, then

(i) the steady-state response is sinusoidal and has the same frequency as the input;
(ii) the output amplitude is $|T(i\omega)|a$;
(iii) the phase shift between output and input is $\arg T(i\omega)$.

The harmonic-response characteristics of such a system are thus completely determined by the values assumed by the appropriate transfer function on the imaginary axis of the s-plane. This result implies that the function $T(i\omega)$ can be found experimentally by subjecting a system to harmonic excitation and measuring the amplitude ratio and phase shift between output and input as the input frequency is varied in the range $0 < \omega < +\infty$.

The importance of this result in the present context lies in the fact that it provides a link between the experimentally-determined harmonic-response characteristics of a system and the investigation of its stability by means of the encirclement theorem. However, it is obvious that it would be pointless to contemplate the use of this link as a means of deciding the stability of a system on the basis of the results of harmonic-response tests performed on the *complete* system; for if a system is unstable this will become apparent as soon as any tests are attempted and there will be no need for any further interpretation of the test results.† Nevertheless, the result contained in (3.32) is frequently useful in situations where it is desired to infer information regarding the stability of a composite system consisting of a number of stable sub-systems from the harmonic-response characteristics of the individual sub-systems. Thus, for example, if a closed-loop control system is asymptotically stable when operating in its open-loop configuration, its open-loop harmonic-response characteristics can be determined and then used in conjunction with the encirclement theorem to predict the stability of the complete closed-loop system.

Problems

1. Use the encirclement theorem to analyse the stability of systems having the following characteristic equations:

   (a) $s^3 + 2s^2 + 3s + 1 = 0$.
   (b) $s^4 + 2s^3 + 3s^2 + s + 2 = 0$.
   (c) $s^4 + s^3 + 3s^2 + s + 2 = 0$.

   Check your results by means of Leonhard's criterion.

2. Investigate the stability of systems having the following transfer functions between input and output:

   (a) $\dfrac{1}{s^2 + s + 1}$

   (b) $\dfrac{s - 1}{s^3 + 4s^2 + s + 2}$

   (c) $\dfrac{s + 1}{2s^3 + s^2 + s + 1}$

---

† Indeed, the concept of steady-state harmonic response has no meaning in the case of an unstable system.

3. Use Nyquist's criterion to analyse the stability of unity-feedback closed-loop control systems having the following open-loop transfer functions:

(a) $\dfrac{s + 2}{s^2 + 2s - 1}$

(d) $\dfrac{2s + 1}{s^2(s + 1)(s + 4)}$

(b) $\dfrac{s(s - 1)}{(s + 2)(s + 4)}$

(e) $\dfrac{s^2 + s + 1}{s^3(s^2 + s + 2)}$

(c) $\dfrac{5}{s(s + \ )(s + 3)}$

4. A closed-loop control system with unity feedback has an open-loop transfer function of the form

$$G(s) = \frac{\xi}{(\tau s + 1)^n} \quad (\xi, \tau > 0),$$

where ξ is the open-loop gain, τ is a time-constant, and n is a positive integer. Show that the closed-loop system will be asymptotically stable for all ξ and τ if $n \leqslant 2$, but that this will be the case only when

$$\xi < \sec^n\left(\frac{\pi}{n}\right)$$

if $n \geqslant 3$.

5. Define contours in the s-plane which, when used in conjunction with the encirclement theorem, make it possible to investigate the degree of stability of a stable linear system by determining
   (a) whether all the roots of the appropriate characteristic equation have real parts less than some negative value $-\sigma_0$;
   (b) whether all the complex characteristic roots give rise to components of impulse response having damping parameters greater than some positive value v_0.

6. Determine the values of the imaginary roots of the characteristic equation
$$F(s) = s^5 + 6s^4 + 12s^3 + 12s^2 + 11s + 6 = 0$$

by plotting the $F(i\omega)$-locus and noting the values of ω for which this locus passes through the origin. Hence, by applying the encirclement theorem to a modified stability contour which avoids the roots on the imaginary axis, show that the system governed by this characteristic equation is marginally stable.

Chapter 4

ROUTH'S CRITERION

4.1 Introduction

In the last chapter it was shown that the number of roots of the characteristic equation

$$F(s) = a_0 s^n + a_1 s^{n-1} + \ldots + a_{n-1} s + a_n = 0 \qquad (4.1)$$

lying in the right half of the s-plane is given by

$$k = \frac{1}{2}\left\{ n - \frac{1}{\pi}[\Delta\Phi]_{-\infty}^{+\infty} \right\}, \qquad (4.2)$$

where $\Phi(\omega) = \arg F(i\omega)$. This result is valid for equations with real or complex coefficients provided there are no roots on the imaginary axis.

Although in principle the direct method of determining $[\Delta\Phi]_{-\infty}^{+\infty}$ by plotting the $F(i\omega)$-locus can always be used, in practice this is often a rather tedious task. It is therefore natural to investigate the possibility of calculating $[\Delta\Phi]_{-\infty}^{+\infty}$ (and thence k) by an alternative method. Routh† devised such a method and formulated it as an algorithm which makes it possible to compute k by means of a purely algebraic manipulation of the coefficients in the characteristic equation. This algorithm can be obtained by first expressing $[\Delta\Phi]_{-\infty}^{+\infty}$ as a Cauchy index and then evaluating this index by means of Sturm's theorem. Although Routh's criterion in its original form can be applied only to real polynomials, it will be shown that the mathematical results upon which the criterion is based can be used to analyse the stability of systems with complex characteristic polynomials.

4.2 Cauchy indices

The *Cauchy index* of a real rational function $f(\omega)$ between the limits $\omega = a$ and $\omega = b$ is written

$$I_a^b f(\omega).$$

† E. J. Routh, *On the Stability of a given state of motion*, Macmillan, 1877.

It is defined as the number of jumps of $f(\omega)$ from $-\infty$ to $+\infty$ minus the number of jumps from $+\infty$ to $-\infty$ as ω increases from a to b.

This definition of a Cauchy index can be illustrated by considering the function

$$f(\omega) = \frac{3\omega + 4}{(\omega + 3)(\omega - 2)} \equiv \frac{1}{(\omega + 3)} + \frac{2}{(\omega - 2)}$$

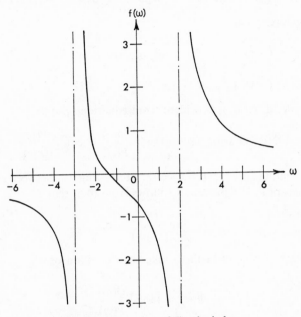

Fig. 4.1. Illustration of Cauchy index.

whose graph is plotted in Fig. 4.1. Since $f(\omega)$ jumps from $-\infty$ to $+\infty$ each time one of the vertical asymptotes is crossed in the direction of increasing ω, it is clear from Fig. 4.1 that, for example,

$$I_{-4}^{-2} f(\omega) = 1,$$

$$I_{-2}^{1} f(\omega) = 0,$$

$$I_{1}^{3} f(\omega) = 1,$$

$$I_{-\infty}^{+\infty} f(\omega) = 2.$$

In order to express the angle $[\Delta\Phi]_{-\infty}^{+\infty}$ as a Cauchy index, it is convenient to write the characteristic polynomial $F(s)$ in the form

$$F(s) = A_0 s^n + B_0 s^{n-1} + A_1 s^{n-2} + B_1 s^{n-3} + \ldots. \qquad (4.3)$$

If the A_r and B_r are real, then

$$F(i\omega) = P(\omega) + iQ(\omega), \qquad (4.4)$$

where

$$\left.\begin{aligned}
P(\omega) &= (-1)^{n/2}(A_0\omega^n - A_1\omega^{n-2} + A_2\omega^{n-4} - \ldots) \\
Q(\omega) &= (-1)^{\frac{n}{2}-1}(B_0\omega^{n-1} - B_1\omega^{n-3} + B_2\omega^{n-5} - \ldots)
\end{aligned}\right\} \qquad (4.5)$$

when n is even, and

$$\left.\begin{aligned}
P(\omega) &= (-1)^{\frac{n-1}{2}}(B_0\omega^{n-1} - B_1\omega^{n-3} + B_2\omega^{n-5} - \ldots) \\
Q(\omega) &= (-1)^{\frac{n-1}{2}}(A_0\omega^n - A_1\omega^{n-2} + A_2\omega^{n-4} - \ldots)
\end{aligned}\right\} \qquad (4.6)$$

when n is odd. Also, it is evident from equation (4.4) that

$$\Phi(\omega) = \arg F(i\omega) = \tan^{-1}\frac{Q(\omega)}{P(\omega)} = \cot^{-1}\frac{P(\omega)}{Q(\omega)}.$$

In evaluating $[\Delta\Phi]^{+\infty}_{-\infty}$ it is necessary to distinguish between even and odd values of n. If n is even, it follows from (4.5) that

$$\lim_{\omega\to\pm\infty}\frac{Q(\omega)}{P(\omega)} = 0. \qquad (4.7)$$

In this case it is convenient to take the definition of $\arg F(i\omega)$ in the form

$$\Phi(\omega) = \tan^{-1}\frac{Q(\omega)}{P(\omega)}.$$

The graph showing $\Phi(\omega)$ as a function of $Q(\omega)/P(\omega)$ then has the form indicated in Fig. 4.2. It follows from (4.7) that $\Phi(+\infty)$ must be represented by one of the points $O, C_1, C_2, \ldots, D_1, D_2, \ldots$, on the $\Phi(\omega)$-axis, as also must $\Phi(-\infty)$. It may therefore be deduced that

$$[\Delta\Phi]^{+\infty}_{-\infty} = r\pi, \qquad (4.8)$$

where r is a positive or negative integer, or zero. Furthermore, it can be seen from Fig. 4.2 that whenever $\Phi(\omega)$ increases by π as a result of moving between any pair of adjacent points on the $\Phi(\omega)$-axis, $Q(\omega)/P(\omega)$ makes one jump from $+\infty$ to $-\infty$; and that whenever $\Phi(\omega)$ decreases by π in a similar fashion, $Q(\omega)/P(\omega)$ makes one jump from $-\infty$ to $+\infty$. Hence, when n is even, equation (4.8) has the explicit form

$$[\Delta\Phi]^{+\infty}_{-\infty} = \left\{-I^{+\infty}_{-\infty}\frac{Q(\omega)}{P(\omega)}\right\}\pi$$

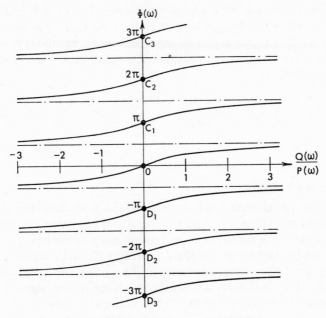

Fig. 4.2. Graph of $\Phi(\omega) = \tan^{-1} Q(\omega)/P(\omega)$.

and substituting for $P(\omega)$ and $Q(\omega)$ from (4.5) yields

$$\frac{1}{\pi}[\Delta\Phi]_{-\infty}^{+\infty} = I_{-\infty}^{+\infty}\frac{B_0\omega^{n-1} - B_1\omega^{n-3} + \cdots}{A_0\omega^n - A_1\omega^{n-2} + \cdots}. \qquad (4.9)$$

If n is odd, it follows from (4.6) that

$$\lim_{\omega \to \pm\infty} \frac{P(\omega)}{Q(\omega)} = 0.$$

In this case it is convenient to take the definition of arg $F(i\omega)$ in the form

$$\Phi(\omega) = \cot^{-1}\frac{P(\omega)}{Q(\omega)}.$$

By similar reasoning to that used for the previous case, it can be shown that

$$[\Delta\Phi]_{-\infty}^{+\infty} = \left\{ I_{-\infty}^{+\infty}\frac{P(\omega)}{Q(\omega)} \right\}\pi$$

when n is odd. Substituting for $P(\omega)$ and $Q(\omega)$ from (4.6) then yields

$$\frac{1}{\pi}[\Delta\Phi]_{-\infty}^{+\infty} = I_{-\infty}^{+\infty}\frac{B_0\omega^{n-1} - B_1\omega^{n-3} + \cdots}{A_0\omega^n - A_1\omega^{n-2} + \cdots}. \qquad (4.10)$$

It can now be seen by comparing the expressions in (4.9) and (4.10) that the value of $[\Delta\Phi]_{-\infty}^{+\infty}/\pi$ is given by the same Cauchy index regardless of whether n (the degree of the characteristic equation) is odd or even. It follows that, in terms of this index, equation (4.2) can be written quite generally as

$$I_{-\infty}^{+\infty}\frac{B_0\omega^{n-1} - B_1\omega^{n-3} + \cdots}{A_0\omega^n - A_1\omega^{n-2} + \cdots} = n - 2k. \qquad (4.11)$$

4.3   Sturm's theorem

In order to calculate k it now only remains to evaluate the Cauchy index in (4.11). This can be done by using *Sturm's theorem*. This theorem is concerned with sequences of real polynomials of the type generated by modifying slightly the standard procedure (Euclid's algorithm) for finding the highest common factor of two polynomials by repeated division. The modification consists in changing the sign of each remainder before using it as the divisor in the next division.

If this modified procedure is carried out for two polynomials $f_1(\omega)$ and $f_2(\omega)$, let the remainder on dividing $f_1(\omega)$ by $f_2(\omega)$ be $-f_3(\omega)$ and the quotient be $q_1(\omega)$, i.e.,

$$f_1(\omega) \equiv q_1(\omega)f_2(\omega) - f_3(\omega) \qquad (4.12a)$$

Similarly, let the remainder on dividing $f_2(\omega)$ by $f_3(\omega)$ be $-f_4(\omega)$ and the quotient be $q_2(\omega)$, and so on. Thus,

$$\left. \begin{array}{l} f_2(\omega) \equiv q_2(\omega)f_3(\omega) - f_4(\omega), \\ \cdot\ \ \cdot\ \ \cdot\ \ \cdot\ \ \cdot\ \ \cdot\ \ \cdot\ \ \cdot \\ f_{r-1}(\omega) \equiv q_{r-1}(\omega)f_r(\omega) - f_{r+1}(\omega), \\ \cdot\ \ \cdot\ \ \cdot\ \ \cdot\ \ \cdot\ \ \cdot\ \ \cdot\ \ \cdot\ \ \cdot \\ f_{m-1}(\omega) \equiv q_{m-1}(\omega)f_m(\omega), \end{array} \right\} \qquad (4.12b)$$

where $f_m(\omega)$ is the last remainder that does not vanish identically.

This process of repeated division clearly defines a sequence of polynomials

$$f_1(\omega), \quad f_2(\omega), \quad f_3(\omega), \quad \ldots, \quad f_m(\omega). \qquad (4.13)$$

If $f_m(\omega)$ is a constant, $f_1(\omega)$ and $f_2(\omega)$ have no common factor and are said to be *co-prime*. If $f_m(\omega)$ is not a constant, this polynomial is the highest common factor of $f_1(\omega)$ and $f_2(\omega)$.

As an example, consider the polynomials

$$f_1(\omega) = \omega^4 - \omega^2 + 3 \qquad (4.14a)$$

and

$$f_2(\omega) = \omega^3 - 2\omega. \qquad (4.14b)$$

Dividing $f_1(\omega)$ by $f_2(\omega)$ gives

$$f_1(\omega) \equiv \omega f_2(\omega) - (-\omega^2 - 3)$$

indicating that, in the notation of (4.12),

$$f_3(\omega) = -\omega^2 - 3. \qquad (4.14c)$$

Dividing $f_2(\omega)$ by $f_3(\omega)$ now gives

$$f_2(\omega) \equiv -\omega f_3(\omega) - 5\omega$$

so that

$$f_4(\omega) = 5\omega. \qquad (4.14d)$$

Finally, dividing $f_3(\omega)$ by $f_4(\omega)$ gives

$$f_3(\omega) \equiv -\tfrac{1}{5}\omega f_4(\omega) - 3$$

indicating that

$$f_5(\omega) = 3. \qquad (4.14e)$$

The process terminates at this stage because there is no remainder when $f_4(\omega)$ is divided by $f_5(\omega)$. Since $f_5(\omega)$ is a constant, the polynomials $f_1(\omega)$ and $f_2(\omega)$ are co-prime.

Sequences of polynomials like (4.14) obtained in this way have certain special properties. To investigate these let it first be assumed that $f_1(\omega)$ and $f_2(\omega)$ are co-prime, so that the final polynomial $f_m(\omega)$ in the general sequence (4.13) is a non-zero constant. Now if there is a value of ω for which $f_{r-1}(\omega) = 0 = f_r(\omega)$, it follows from (4.12) that also $f_{r+1}(\omega) = 0$. But from the fact that $f_r(\omega) = 0 = f_{r+1}(\omega)$ it may similarly be deduced that $f_{r+2}(\omega) = 0$, and so on. Ultimately, this reasoning leads to the conclusion that $f_m(\omega) = 0$, which is a contradiction. It follows that the premise of the foregoing argument must be false and therefore that no two successive polynomials in the sequence (4.13) can vanish for the same value of ω. Again, if $f_r(\omega) = 0$ it may be deduced from (4.12) that $f_{r-1}(\omega) = -f_{r+1}(\omega)$. Hence, if any function of the sequence (4.13) vanishes, the two adjacent functions do not vanish and have opposite signs. A sequence of polynomials having these properties is called a *Sturm sequence*. It can be readily verified that the polynomials (4.14) constitute a Sturm sequence. Thus, for example, $f_2(\sqrt{2}) = 0$ and $f_1(\sqrt{2}) = -f_3(\sqrt{2}) = 5$.

If the polynomials $f_1(\omega)$ and $f_2(\omega)$ are not co-prime, so that $f_m(\omega)$ is not a constant, the sequence (4.13) is called a *generalised Sturm sequence*. Such a sequence becomes an ordinary Sturm sequence if all the polynomials are divided by $f_m(\omega)$.

It is now possible to prove Sturm's theorem. Thus, let the polynomials in (4.13) form a Sturm sequence, and let $V(\omega)$ be the number of sign variations in the sequence when the polynomials are evaluated for a fixed value of ω. The only occasion when $V(\omega)$ can change is when ω passes through a zero of one of the polynomials. However, if $f_r(c) = 0$ (c a constant), then $f_{r-1}(c)$ and $f_{r+1}(c)$ will have opposite signs which they will retain throughout an interval $c - \varepsilon < \omega < c + \varepsilon$ provided that ε is sufficiently small. It follows that the value of $V(\omega)$ cannot change when ω passes through a zero of any of the polynomials $f_2(\omega), f_3(\omega),$ $\ldots, f_{m-2}(\omega), f_{m-1}(\omega)$. Moreover, $f_m(\omega)$ is never zero (by hypothesis) and so cannot affect $V(\omega)$. However, the remaining polynomial $f_1(\omega)$ *can* vanish; and when $f_1(\omega)$ passes through zero $V(\omega)$ decreases by unity if $f_2(\omega)/f_1(\omega)$ jumps from $-\infty$ to $+\infty$, and increases by unity if the jump is from $+\infty$ to $-\infty$. Hence, if ω increases from a to b, $V(b)$ will be less than $V(a)$ by an amount equal to the Cauchy index of $f_2(\omega)/f_1(\omega)$ between a and b, i.e.,

$$V(a) - V(b) = I_a^b \frac{f_2(\omega)}{f_1(\omega)}. \tag{4.15}$$

This is *Sturm's theorem* for the Sturm sequence (4.13). It can be shown that the theorem is also valid for generalised Sturm sequences.

Sturm's theorem can be used to evaluate the Cauchy index

$$I_{-\infty}^{+\infty} \frac{B_0\omega^{n-1} - B_1\omega^{n-3} + \ldots}{A_0\omega^n - A_1\omega^{n-2} + \ldots} \tag{4.16}$$

which appears in equation (4.11) by taking

$$\left.\begin{aligned} f_1(\omega) &= A_0\omega^n - A_1\omega^{n-2} + \ldots, \\ f_2(\omega) &= B_0\omega^{n-1} - B_1\omega^{n-3} + \ldots, \end{aligned}\right\} \tag{4.17}$$

and then obtaining by repeated division the remaining polynomials $f_3(\omega), \ldots, f_m(\omega)$ of the Sturm sequence generated by $f_1(\omega)$ and $f_2(\omega)$. In fact, if $V(\omega)$ is the number of sign variations in this sequence when ω has a fixed value, it follows from Sturm's theorem that the Cauchy index (4.16) is equal to

$$V(-\infty) - V(+\infty). \tag{4.18}$$

The value of k (i.e., the number of characteristic roots in the right half-plane) can then be found by substituting this value for the index in equation (4.11).

This technique can be illustrated by applying Sturm's theorem to the characteristic equation

$$F(s) = s^4 + s^3 + s^2 + 2s + 3 = 0 \qquad (4.19)$$

previously studied in Section 3.2. In this case, substituting $s = i\omega$ indicates that, in the notation of equations (4.17),

$$f_1(\omega) = \omega^4 - \omega^2 + 3 \qquad (4.20a)$$

and

$$f_2(\omega) = \omega^3 - 2\omega. \qquad (4.20b)$$

The remaining functions in the Sturm sequence generated by these polynomials have already been found, and are seen from equations (4.14) to be

$$f_3(\omega) = -\omega^2 - 3, \qquad (4.20c)$$

$$f_4(\omega) = 5\omega, \qquad (4.20d)$$

$$f_5(\omega) = 3. \qquad (4.20e)$$

When $\omega = +\infty$, the signs of the polynomials (4.20) are $+, +, -, +, +$ so that $V(+\infty) = 2$; when $\omega = -\infty$, the signs are $+, -, -, -, +$ so that $V(-\infty) = 2$. Hence, by Sturm's theorem,

$$I_{-\infty}^{+\infty} \frac{\omega^3 - 2\omega}{\omega^4 - \omega^2 + 3} = V(-\infty) - V(+\infty) = 2 - 2 = 0.$$

Substituting this value into equation (4.11), and also putting $n = 4$, finally gives $k = 2$. Equation (4.19) therefore has two roots in the right half of the s-plane and so represents an unstable system. This result agrees with that obtained in Section 3.2 by direct determination of the angle $[\Delta\Phi]_{-\infty}^{+\infty}$.

4.4 Routh's array

The stability problem has now been reduced to that of evaluating the Cauchy index (4.16) by means of Sturm's theorem. This in turn requires the construction of the Sturm sequence generated by the polynomials $f_1(\omega)$ and $f_2(\omega)$ defined in equations (4.17). It will now be shown that it is not necessary to construct this sequence by explicit repeated long division since it is possible to deduce a general rule which schematises the necessary computations and reduces them to simple operations.

If $f_1(\omega)$ is divided by $f_2(\omega)$ and the negative remainder is taken as $f_3(\omega)$ (in accordance with 4.12a)), it is found that

$$f_3(\omega) = C_0\omega^{n-2} - C_1\omega^{n-4} + \ldots,$$

where

$$C_0 = \frac{B_0A_1 - A_0B_1}{B_0}, \qquad C_1 = \frac{B_0A_2 - A_0B_2}{B_0}, \ldots \qquad (4.21)$$

Similarly, if $f_2(\omega)$ is divided by $f_3(\omega)$ and the negative remainder is taken as $f_4(\omega)$, it is found that

$$f_4(\omega) = D_0\omega^{n-3} - D_1\omega^{n-5} + \ldots,$$

where

$$D_0 = \frac{C_0B_1 - B_0C_1}{C_0}, \qquad D_1 = \frac{C_0B_2 - B_0C_2}{C_0}, \ldots \qquad (4.22)$$

In view of the form of the coefficients given in (4.21) and (4.22), it is possible to infer a general expression relating the coefficients in any three successive polynomials in the Sturm sequence generated by $f_1(\omega)$ and $f_2(\omega)$. Thus, if the coefficients in $f_{r-1}(\omega)$ and $f_r(\omega)$ are U_0, U_1, U_2, $\ldots$, and V_0, V_1, V_2, $\ldots$, respectively, the coefficients in the next polynomial $f_{r+1}(\omega)$ are given by

$$W_j = \frac{V_0U_{j+1} - U_0V_{j+1}}{V_0} \; (j = 0, 1, 2, \ldots). \qquad (4.23)$$

The polynomial itself has the explicit form

$$f_{r+1}(\omega) = W_0\omega^{n-r} - W_1\omega^{n-r-2} + W_2\omega^{n-r-4} - \ldots \qquad (4.24)$$

The formula (4.23) suggests a simple diagrammatic representation of the calculation of the coefficients in the polynomials of the required Sturm sequence. Thus, if the coefficients in $f_{r-1}(\omega)$ and $f_r(\omega)$ are written in successive rows, the coefficients in $f_{r+1}(\omega)$ can be found by performing the processes of cross-multiplication, subtraction, and division implied by (4.23) and indicated in the scheme (4.25a):

$$
\begin{array}{lcccccc}
f_{r-1}(\omega): & U_0 & U_1 & U_2 & \ldots & U_j & U_{j+1} & \ldots \\
f_r(\omega): & V_0 & V_1 & V_2 & \ldots & V_j & V_{j+1} & \ldots \\
f_{r+1}(\omega): & W_0 & W_1 & W_2 & \ldots & \boxed{W_j} & W_{j+1} & \ldots
\end{array}
\qquad (4.25a)
$$

Starting with $f_1(\omega)$ and $f_2(\omega)$, it is therefore possible to compute the coefficients in $f_3(\omega)$ by using (4.23). The coefficients in $f_4(\omega)$ can then be calculated from $f_2(\omega)$ and $f_3(\omega)$, and the process repeated until the

last polynominial $f_m(\omega)$ is reached. The complete array of coefficients
obtained in this way has the form

$$
\left.
\begin{array}{cccc}
A_0 & A_1 & A_2 & \cdots \\
B_0 & B_1 & B_2 & \cdots \\
C_0 & C_1 & C_2 & \cdots \\
D_0 & D_1 & D_2 & \cdots \\
\cdot & \cdot & \cdot & \cdots \\
\cdot & \cdot & \cdot & \cdots
\end{array}
\right\}
\qquad (4.25b)
$$

and is known as *Routh's array*.

As an example of the determination of a Sturm sequence by means
of Routh's array, consider again the equation

$$ F(s) = s^4 + s^3 + s^2 + 2s + 3 = 0. \qquad (4.26) $$

In this case, $f_1(\omega) = \omega^4 - \omega^2 + 3$ and $f_2(\omega) = \omega^3 - 2\omega$. The first
two rows of Routh's array are accordingly

$$
\begin{array}{lccc}
\omega^4: & 1 & 1 & 3 \\
\omega^3: & 1 & 2
\end{array}
$$

where the highest power of ω occurring in any given polynomial is
indicated to the left of the array. It follows from (4.23) and (4.25) that
the next row is given by

$$ C_0 = \frac{1 \times 1 - 1 \times 2}{1} = -1, \qquad C_1 = \frac{1 \times 3 - 1 \times 0}{1} = 3, $$

indicating that $f_3(\omega) = -\omega^2 - 3$. Routh's array is now

$$
\begin{array}{lccc}
\omega^4: & 1 & 1 & 3 \\
\omega^3: & 1 & 2 \\
\omega^2: & -1 & 3
\end{array}
$$

Proceeding to the next row gives

$$ D_0 = \frac{-1 \times 2 - 1 \times 3}{-1} = 5, \qquad D_1 = \frac{-1 \times 0 - 1 \times 0}{-1} = 0, $$

so that $f_4(\omega) = 5\omega$. Routh's array is now

$$
\begin{array}{lccc}
\omega^4: & 1 & 1 & 3 \\
\omega^3: & 1 & 2 \\
\omega^2: & -1 & 3 \\
\omega_1: & 5
\end{array}
$$

The next row is given by

$$E_0 = \frac{5 \times 3 - (-1) \times 0}{5} = 3, \qquad E_1 = \frac{5 \times 0 - (-1) \times 0}{5} = 0,$$

indicating that $f_5(\omega) = 3$. Routh's array is now

$$
\begin{array}{lrrr}
\omega^4: & 1 & 1 & 3 \\
\omega^3: & 1 & 2 & \\
\omega^2: & -1 & 3 & \\
\omega^1: & 5 & & \\
\omega^0: & 3 & &
\end{array}
$$

The calculation terminates at this point since the next polynomial is identically zero. The last array is thus the complete Routh array for equation (4.26).

It will be noted that the Sturm sequence calculated by Routh's array is identical to that obtained previously by long division. However, Routh's array provides a much more rapid means of determining this sequence. Furthermore, it will be shown that the stability of a system can be deduced from Routh's array simply by examining the signs of the quantities in its first column.

4.5 Routh's criterion

The Sturm sequence

$$f_1(\omega), f_2(\omega), f_3(\omega), \ldots, f_m(\omega) \tag{4.27}$$

is said to be *non-singular* if $m = n + 1$, where n is the degree of the characteristic equation $F(s) = 0$. In this case, the degree of each polynomial in (4.27) is one less than that of its predecessor and the last function, $f_m(\omega)$, is a constant. In terms of Routh's array, the non-singular case is characterised by the termination of the array after precisely $(n + 1)$ rows.

Since $f_m(\omega)$ is a constant in the non-singular case, it follows that $f_1(\omega)$ and $f_2(\omega)$, and therefore $P(\omega)$ and $Q(\omega)$ (see equations (4.4), (4.5) and (4.6)), are co-prime. The latter functions consequently have no common factor and therefore do not vanish simultaneously for any value of ω. In particular,

$$F(i\omega) = P(\omega) + iQ(\omega)$$

does not vanish for any *real* value of ω. It follows that $F(s) = 0$ has no imaginary roots in the non-singular case, so that equation (4.11) is valid† and may be combined with (4.18) to give

$$n - 2k = V(-\infty) - V(-\infty). \tag{4.28}$$

In equation (4.28), $V(\omega)$ is the number of sign variations in the Sturm sequence (4.27) when ω has a fixed value.

Now the highest power of ω occurring in any polynomial $f_r(\omega)$ of (4.27) is ω^{n-r+1}. Hence, when $\omega = +\infty$ the sign of $f_r(\omega)$ is the same as that of the coefficient of ω^{n-r+1}, and when $\omega = -\infty$ it differs from it by a factor $(-1)^{n-r+1}$. The required numbers of sign variations are therefore given by

$$\left.\begin{aligned} V(+\infty) &= v(A_0, B_0, C_0, \ldots), \\ V(-\infty) &= v(-A_0, B_0, -C_0, \ldots), \end{aligned}\right\} \tag{4.29}$$

where $A_0, B_0, C_0, \ldots$, are the leading coefficients in the polynomials $f_1(\omega), f_2(\omega), f_3(\omega), \ldots$, and $v(\alpha, \beta, \gamma, \ldots)$ is the number of sign variations in the sequence $\alpha, \beta, \gamma, \ldots$. Now

$$V(-\infty) = n - V(+\infty) \tag{4.30}$$

since, in the non-singular case, there are $(n + 1)$ polynomials in (4.27) and consequently n possible sign variations. Thus, using equations (4.28), (4.29) and (4.30), it may be deduced that

$$k = v(A_0, B_0, C_0, \ldots),$$

i.e., in the non-singular case, the number of characteristic roots with positive real parts is equal to the number of sign variations in the first column of Routh's array.

A sufficient condition for asymptotic stability is therefore that Routh's array should be non-singular and contain no sign variations in its first column. The above reasoning can be reversed to show that this condition is also necessary. Hence, all the roots of a real characteristic equation $F(s) = 0$ have negative real parts if and only if Routh's array for $F(s)$ is non-singular and has no sign variations in its first column. This is *Routh's criterion*.

As a first illustration of the use of Routh's criterion consider Routh's array for the equation $F(s) = s^4 + s^3 + s^2 + 2s + 3 = 0$ which is given on p. 62. This array has five rows and is therefore non-singular. But since there are two sign variations in its first column, there are two

† It will be recalled that equation (4.11) was derived on the assumption that $F(s) = 0$ has no imaginary roots.

characteristic roots with positive real parts. The system governed by $F(s) = 0$ is consequently unstable.

As a second illustration consider the equation

$$F(s) = s^3 + 6s^2 + 11s + 6 = 0.$$

Routh's array in this case is

$$\begin{array}{lll} \omega^3: & 1 & 11 \\ \omega^2: & 6 & 6 \\ \omega^1: & 10 \\ \omega^0: & 6 \end{array}$$

This array is non-singular since it has four rows. Since also there are no sign variations in its first column, all the characteristic roots have negative real parts. The system governed by $F(s) = 0$ is consequently asymptotically stable.

As a third example, consider the equation

$$F(s) = s^4 + 3s^3 + 6s^2 + 12s + 8.$$

In this case Routh's array begins.

$$\begin{array}{llll} \omega^4: & 1 & 6 & 8 \\ \omega^3: & 3 & 12 \\ \omega^2: & 2 & 8 \end{array}$$

but the next polynomial, $f_4(\omega)$, vanishes identically. The array is therefore singular and so Routh's criterion indicates immediately that characteristic roots with non-negative real parts exist.

4.6 Singular cases

If a zero occurs prematurely† in the first column of Routh's array (as in the last example of the last section), the construction of the remaining rows of the array by the normal method cannot be continued since it would involve division by zero. In fact, if only the asymptotic stability of the system under investigation is in question (and no additional information regarding the characteristic roots is required), it is unnecessary to proceed further with the construction of the array since a singular array immediately indicates instability or, at best, marginal stability. However, it is possible to modify the standard procedure for constructing Routh's array if additional information is required in a singular case.

† i.e., in one of the first $(n + 1)$ rows.

It is necessary to distinguish between two types of singularity in which either all the elements of a row of the array vanish prematurely or only the first element of a row vanishes. These two possibilities require different techniques which will now be discussed in turn.

If in the Sturm sequence (4.27) it is found that $f_{m+1}(\omega) \equiv 0$ for some $m < n + 1$, it follows that the generating polynomials $f_1(\omega)$ and $f_2(\omega)$ are not co-prime and that $f_m(\omega)$ is their highest common factor. Hence, any zero of $f_m(\omega)$ will also be a zero of both $f_1(\omega)$ and $f_2(\omega)$. Since $f_1(\omega)$ and $f_2(\omega)$ vanish if and only if $P(\omega)$ and $Q(\omega)$ vanish, it may therefore be deduced from equation (4.4) that $i\Omega$ will be a zero of the characteristic polynomial $F(s)$ if Ω is a zero of the last non-vanishing polynomial $f_m(\omega)$. In particular, $i\Omega$ will be an imaginary zero of $F(s)$ if Ω is a real zero of $f_m(\omega)$. For example, in the array for the polynomial

$$F(s) = s^4 + 3s^3 + 6s^2 + 12s + 8$$

whose construction was begun at the end of the last section, $f_4(\omega) \equiv 0$ and $f_3(\omega) = 2\omega^2 - 8$. The zeros of $f_3(\omega)$ are obviously ± 2 and it can be verified that, in accordance with the foregoing general reasoning, $\pm 2i$ are zeros of $F(s)$.

Thus, in order to deal with singular cases in which a complete row of Routh's array vanishes prematurely, it is necessary to cater for the possible existence of imaginary characteristic roots. If $F(s) = 0$ has l imaginary roots and k roots with positive real parts, it can be shown that equation (4.11) becomes

$$I_{-\infty}^{+\infty} \frac{f_2(\omega)}{f_1(\omega)} = n - 2k - l, \tag{4.31}$$

where $f_1(\omega)$ and $f_2(\omega)$ are as defined in (4.17).

If it is assumed that $f_m(\omega)$ (the highest common factor of $f_1(\omega)$ and $f_2(\omega)$) has q unrepeated zeros $\Omega_1, \Omega_2, \ldots, \Omega_q$, then $f_m(\omega)$ can be written in the form

$$f_m(\omega) = c \prod_{r=1}^{q} (\omega - \Omega_r), \tag{4.32}$$

where c is a constant. If it is further assumed that the first l of these zeros are real, it follows that the imaginary zeros of the characteristic polynomial $F(s)$ are $i\Omega_1, i\Omega_2, \ldots, i\Omega_l$.

Now, by differentiating (4.32) with respect to ω, it is evident that

$$f'_m(\omega) = c(\omega - \Omega_2)(\omega - \Omega_3) \ldots (\omega - \Omega_q)$$
$$+ c(\omega - \Omega_1)(\omega - \Omega_3) \ldots (\omega - \Omega_q)$$
$$+ \quad . \quad . \quad . \quad . \quad . \quad . \quad . \quad .$$
$$+ c(\omega - \Omega_1)(\omega - \Omega_2) \ldots (\omega - \Omega_{q-1})$$

and consequently that

$$\frac{f'_m(\omega)}{f_m(\omega)} = \sum_{r=1}^{q} \left(\frac{1}{\omega - \Omega_r} \right).$$

Since only the first l of the Ω_r are real, it follows that

$$I_{-\infty}^{+\infty} \frac{f'_m(\omega)}{f_m(\omega)} = l.$$

If this result is combined with that given in (4.31) it is found that

$$I_{-\infty}^{+\infty} \frac{f_2(\omega)}{f_1(\omega)} + I_{-\infty}^{+\infty} \frac{f'_m(\omega)}{f_m(\omega)} = n - 2k.$$

This equation indicates that Routh's array can be completed by calculating $f'_m(\omega)$ and then forming a sub-array for $f_m(\omega)$ and $f'_m(\omega)$ in the usual way.

This technique can be conveniently illustrated by completing Routh's array for the polynomial $F(s) = s^4 + 3s^3 + 6s^2 + 12s + 8$ discussed previously. In this example, $f_4(\omega) \equiv 0$ and $f_3(\omega) = 2\omega^2 - 8$ so that $f'_3(\omega) = 4\omega$. The complete array is therefore

$$
\begin{array}{lll}
\omega^4: & 1 & 6 & 8 \\
\omega^3: & 3 & 12 \\
\omega^2: & 2 & 8 \\
\omega^1: & 4 \\
\omega^0: & 8 \\
\end{array}
$$

Since there are no sign variations in the first column, there are no characteristic roots with positive real parts. Nevertheless, $F(s)$ represents a system which is only marginally stable because of the imaginary roots $s = \pm 2i$ corresponding to the real zeros of $f_3(\omega)$.

The foregoing discussion is based on the assumption that $f_m(\omega)$ has no repeated zeros. If this is not the case, then $f_m(\omega)$ and $f'_m(\omega)$ will have a common factor and Routh's array will again terminate prematurely in a row of zeros. The highest common factor of $f_m(\omega)$ and $f'_m(\omega)$ will be given by the last non-vanishing polynomial, say $g_m(\omega)$. The construction of Routh's array is therefore continued by calculating $g'_m(\omega)$ and then forming a sub-array for $g_m(\omega)$ and $g'_m(\omega)$. It may be necessary to repeat this procedure several times before the complete array (having $(n + 1)$ rows for an nth degree characteristic equation) is obtained.

ONLY FIRST ELEMENT VANISHES

The second type of singularity occurs when only the first element of a row of Routh's array vanishes prematurely. Thus, for example, Routh's array for the polynomial

$$F(s) = s^6 + s^5 + 2s^4 + 2s^3 + 3s^2 + s + 1$$

begins

$$
\begin{array}{llll}
\omega^6: & 1 & 2 & 3 & 1 \\
\omega^5: & 1 & 2 & 1 \\
\omega^4: & 0 & 2 & 1 \\
\end{array}
$$

Because of the zero in the third row, the array is singular and it may therefore be concluded that the system governed by $F(s)$ is not asymptotically stable.

There are several ways of continuing the construction of an array of this type if additional information regarding the characteristic roots is required. One method is to form a new polynomial $G(S) = S^n F(1/S)$ whose zeros $S = 1/s$ are the reciprocals of the zeros of the original polynomial $F(s)$. Now for arbitrary real numbers p and q, $1/(p + iq) \equiv (p - iq)/(p^2 + q^2)$ provided p and q do not both vanish. It follows that $G(S)$ and $F(s)$ have the same number of imaginary zeros and the same number of zeros with positive real parts. As a consequence, Routh's array for $G(S)$ (which will not normally be singular) can be used to investigate the zeros of $F(s)$.

For example, if $F(s) = s^6 + s^5 + 2s^4 + 2s^3 + 3s^2 + s + 1$ then $G(S) = S^6 + S^5 + 3S^4 + 2S^3 + 2S^2 + S + 1$ (note that $G(S)$ can be obtained simply by inverting the order of the coefficients in $F(s)$). Routh's array for $G(S)$ is

$$
\begin{array}{lllll}
\omega^6: & 1 & 3 & 2 & 1 \\
\omega^5: & 1 & 2 & 1 \\
\omega^4: & 1 & 1 & 1 \\
\omega^3: & 1 & 0 \\
\omega^2: & 1 & 1 \\
\omega^1: & -1 \\
\omega^0: & 1 \\
\end{array}
$$

The array is now non-singular but there are two sign variations in the first column. It follows that both $G(S)$ and $F(s)$ have two zeros with positive real parts. The system governed by $F(s)$ is therefore unstable.

If the characteristic polynomial $F(s)$ has symmetric coefficients, then $G(s) \equiv F(s)$. The polynomials $G(S)$ and $F(s)$ will consequently have identical Routh arrays. In particular, the array for $G(S)$ will be singular if the array for $F(s)$ is singular. Thus, if $F(s) = s^4 + s^3 + s^2 + s + 1$, then $G(S) = S^4 + S^3 + S^2 + S + 1$, indicating that $G(s) \equiv F(s)$. Routh's array for both polynomials begins

$$
\begin{array}{llll}
\omega^4: & 1 & 1 & 1 \\
\omega^3: & 1 & 1 \\
\omega^2: & 0 & 1
\end{array}
$$

An impasse of this kind can be avoided by multiplying the original polynomial $F(s)$ by a factor of the form $(s + \alpha)$, where α is a real number. For example, multiplication of the polynomial

$$F(s) = s^4 + s^3 + s^2 + s + 1$$

by a factor $(s + 1)$ produces a new polynomial

$$H(s) = s^5 + 2s^4 + 2s^3 + 2s^2 + 2s + 1.$$

The zeros of $H(s)$ coincide with those of $F(s)$ except for the extra zero $s = -1$, so that $H(s)$ and $F(s)$ have the same number of zeros with positive real parts. Routh's array for $H(s)$ is

$$
\begin{array}{lll}
\omega^5: & 1 & 2 & 2 \\
\omega^4: & 2 & 2 & 1 \\
\omega^3: & 1 & 3/2 \\
\omega^2: & -1 & 1 \\
\omega: & 5/2 \\
\omega^0: & 1
\end{array}
$$

This array is non-singular but there are two sign variations in the first column. It follows that $F(s)$ has two zeros with positive real parts.

4.7 Characteristic equations having complex coefficients

Although Routh's criterion as stated on p. 63 applies only to characteristic equations having real coefficients, the mathematical apparatus of Cauchy indices and Sturm's theorem can be used to investigate the stability of systems governed by complex characteristic equations. Characteristic equations of this type arise in such fields as flutter and shaft-whirling.

If $F(s)$ is a polynomial having complex coefficients, let

$$F(i\omega) = B_0\omega^n + B_1\omega^{n-1} + \ldots + B_n$$
$$+ i(A_0\omega^n + A_1\omega^{n-1} + \ldots + A_n), \quad (4.33)$$

where the A_r and B_r are real numbers. Equation (4.33) can always be arranged so that $A_0 \neq 0$ by replacing $F(s)$ by $iF(s)$ if necessary ($F(s)$ and $iF(s)$ have the same zeros).

If $F(s)$ has no imaginary zeros, the argument leading up to equation (4.2) remains valid in the present case. Thus, if $F(s)$ has k zeros with positive real parts,

$$\frac{1}{\pi}[\Delta\Phi]_{-\infty}^{+\infty} = n - 2k, \quad (4.34)$$

where $[\Delta\Phi]_{-\infty}^{+\infty}$ is the increase in $\Phi(\omega) = \arg F(i\omega)$ as ω increases from $-\infty$ to $+\infty$. Now it follows from equation (4.33) that

$$\Phi(\omega) = \cot^{-1}\frac{B_0\omega^n + B_1\omega^{n-1} + \ldots + B_n}{A_0\omega^n + A_1\omega^{n-1} + \ldots + A_n}$$

and consequently that

$$\frac{1}{\pi}[\Delta\Phi]_{-\infty}^{+\infty} = I_{-\infty}^{+\infty}\frac{B_0\omega^n + B_1\omega^{n-1} + \ldots + B_n}{A_0\omega^n + A_1\omega^{n-1} + \ldots + A_n}. \quad (4.35)$$

If the Cauchy index in (4.35) is evaluated by Sturm's theorem, the value of k can then be found from equation (4.34).

As an example, consider the complex characteristic equation

$$F(s) = s^3 + (1 + i)s^2 + is + 1 = 0 \quad (4.36)$$

for which

$$F(i\omega) = (-\omega^2 - \omega + 1) + i(-\omega^3 - \omega^2).$$

In this case, equation (4.35) has the form

$$\frac{1}{\pi}[\Delta\Phi]_{-\infty}^{+\infty} = I_{-\infty}^{+\infty}\frac{-\omega^2 - \omega + 1}{-\omega^3 - \omega^2}. \quad (4.37)$$

The Cauchy index in (4.37) can be evaluated by applying Sturm's theorem to the Sturm sequence generated from the polynomials

$$f_1(\omega) = -\omega^3 - \omega^2, f_2(\omega) = -\omega^2 - \omega + 1$$

by repeated long division. This sequence is found to be

$$\left.\begin{array}{l} f_1(\omega) = -\omega^3 - \omega^2, \\ f_2(\omega) = -\omega^2 - \omega + 1, \\ f_3(\omega) = \omega \\ f_4(\omega) = -1. \end{array}\right\} \quad (4.38)$$

When $\omega = +\infty$ these polynomials have the signs $-$, $-$, $+$, $-$; there are thus two sign variations so that $V(+\infty) = 2$. Similarly, when $\omega = -\infty$ the polynomials have the signs $+$, $-$, $-$, $-$, indicating that $V(-\infty) = 1$. Hence, by Sturm's theorem (4.15),

$$I_{-\infty}^{+\infty}\frac{-\omega^2 - \omega + 1}{-\omega^3 - \omega^2} = V(-\infty) - V(+\infty) = -1.$$

Using this result in equation (4.37) indicates that

$$\frac{1}{\pi}[\Delta\Phi]_{-\infty}^{+\infty} = -1,$$

so that equation (4.34) becomes

$$-1 = 3 - 2k$$

since also $n = 3$. Hence $k = 2$, i.e., equation (4.36) has two roots with positive real parts and so represents an unstable system.

As a second example of a complex characteristic equation consider

$$F(s) = s^2 + 2v\omega_n s + (\omega_n^2 - 2iv\omega_n\Omega) = 0 \qquad (4.39)$$

which arises in the theory of shaft whirling.† In this equation, v is a damping parameter, ω_n the undamped natural frequency, and Ω the rotational speed of the system. All these parameters are assumed to have positive values.

When $s = i\omega$, equation (4.39) becomes

$$F(i\omega) = (-\omega^2 + \omega_n^2) + i(2v\omega_n\omega - 2v\omega_n\Omega) = 0. \qquad (4.40)$$

Now in deriving (4.35) it was assumed that (in the notation of (4.33)) $A_0 \neq 0$, which is not the case in equation (4.40). However, the last equation can easily be put into the standard form by considering $G(s) \equiv iF(s)$ instead of $F(s)$. This gives

$$G(i\omega) = (-2v\omega_n\omega + 2v\omega_n\Omega) + i(-\omega^2 + \omega_n^2), \qquad (4.41)$$

and it is evident that $F(s)$ and $G(s)$ have the same zeros.

In the case of (4.41), equation (4.35) has the explicit form

$$\frac{1}{\pi}[\Delta\Phi]_{-\infty}^{+\infty} = I_{-\infty}^{+\infty}\frac{-2v\omega_n\omega + 2v\omega_n\Omega}{-\omega^2 + \omega_n^2}. \qquad (4.42)$$

† See R. E. D. Bishop, The vibration of rotating shafts, *J. mech. Engng Sci.*, 1, 50, 1959.

The next polynomial in the Sturm sequence generated by

$$f_1(\omega) = -\omega^2 + \omega_n^2 \qquad (4.43a)$$

and

$$f_2(\omega) = -2v\omega_n\omega + 2v\omega_n\Omega \qquad (4.43b)$$

can be obtained by dividing $f_1(\omega)$ by $f_2(\omega)$. This gives

$$f_1(\omega) \equiv \left(\frac{\omega + \Omega}{2v\omega_n}\right)f_2(\omega) - (\Omega^2 - \omega_n^2)$$

so that the next polynomial in the sequence is

$$f_3(\omega) = \Omega^2 - \omega_n^2. \qquad (4.43c)$$

The sequence terminates at this point since $f_3(\omega)$ is independent of ω.

Since the parameters v and ω_n are positive, it is only necessary to distinguish between the two cases $\Omega > \omega_n$ and $\Omega < \omega_n$ in examining the Sturm sequence (4.43). Thus, when $\Omega > \omega_n$ it is evident that $V(+\infty) = 1$ and $V(-\infty) = 1$. It follows from Sturm's theorem that the Cauchy index in (4.42) is then equal to

$$V(-\infty) - V(+\infty) = 1 - 1 = 0.$$

Equation (4.34) therefore becomes

$$0 = 2 - 2k,$$

giving $k = 1$. This indicates that when $\Omega > \omega_n$ equation (4.39) has one root with a positive real part and so represents an unstable system.

However, when $\Omega < \omega_n$ it may be inferred from (4.43) that $V(+\infty) = 0$ and $V(-\infty) = 2$. It follows from Sturm's theorem that the Cauchy index in (4.42) is then equal to

$$V(-\infty) - V(+\infty) = 2 - 0 = 2.$$

Substituting this value into equation (4.34) gives

$$2 = 2 - 2k$$

from which it follows that $k = 0$. Hence, when $\Omega < \omega_n$ equation (4.39) has no roots with positive real parts and so represents an asymptotically stable system since the characteristic equation has an imaginary root only when $\Omega = \omega_n$. The system will therefore by asymptotically stable if and only if the rotational speed is less than the undamped natural frequency.

M.E.M. 1.—6

Problems

1. Use Sturm's theorem to evaluate the Cauchy index

$$I_{-\infty}^{+\infty} \frac{5\omega^3 - 7\omega}{\omega^4 - 9\omega^2 + 2},$$

and hence show that all the roots of the equation

$$s^4 + 5s^3 + 9s^2 + 7s + 2 = 0$$

have negative real parts. Check your results by means of Routh's criterion.

2. Investigate the location of the roots of the following equations by means of Routh's criterion:

(a) $s^3 + 2s^2 + 2s + 1 = 0$.
(b) $s^3 + 2s^2 + s + 2 = 0$.
(c) $s^5 + s^4 + s^3 + s^2 + s + 1 = 0$.
(d) $s^5 + s^4 + 3s^3 + 3s^2 + 1 = 0$.
(e) $s^6 + 2s^5 + 2s^4 + 4s^3 + s^2 + s + 1 = 0$.

3. If $a_0 > 0$ in each of the following characteristic equations, use Routh's criterion to prove that the stated conditions are necessary and sufficient for asymptotic stability:

(a) $a_0s^2 + a_1s + a_2 = 0$; $a_1 > 0$, $a_2 > 0$.
(b) $a_0s^3 + a_1s^2 + a_2s + a_3 = 0$;
    $a_1 > 0$, $a_3 > 0$, $a_1a_2 - a_0a_3 > 0$.

4. A closed-loop control system with unity feedback has an open-loop transfer function of the form

$$G(s) = \frac{\xi}{s(s + 1)(s + 2)(s + 3)},$$

where ξ is the open-loop gain. Calculate the value of ξ which will result in the characteristic equation of the closed-loop system having a pair of conjugate imaginary roots, and determine all four roots when ξ has this value.

5. A system whose behaviour is in certain respects analogous to that of a whirling shaft consists of a particle moving on the inner surface of a spherical bowl which rotates about its vertical axis with uniform angular velocity Ω.† The equations of motion of the particle for

† H. Lamb, On kinetic stability, *Proc. R. Soc. A.*, **80**, 168, 1908.

small excursions from O, the lowest point of the bowl, have the form

$$\left.\begin{aligned}
\frac{d^2x}{dt^2} + 2v\omega_n \frac{dx}{dt} + (\omega_n^2 - \Omega^2)x - 2\Omega \frac{dy}{dt} &= 0, \\
\frac{d^2y}{dt^2} + 2v\omega_n \frac{dy}{dt} + (\omega_n^2 - \Omega^2)y + 2\Omega \frac{dx}{dt} &= 0,
\end{aligned}\right\}$$

when the motion is referred to horizontal rectangular axes Ox, Oy which rotate with the bowl: in these equations, ω_n is the frequency of free undamped oscillations of the particle about O, and $v(> 0)$ is a dimensionless viscous damping parameter. By introducing a new coordinate $z = x + iy$ show that the characteristic equation of this system can be expressed in the complex form

$$s^2 + (2i\Omega + 2v\omega_n)s + (\omega_n^2 - \Omega^2) = 0,$$

and use Sturm's theorem to show that it is necessary and sufficient for asymptotic stability that $\Omega < \omega_n$. How would the particle move if $\Omega > \omega_n$?

Chapter 5

HURWITZ'S CRITERION

5.1 Introduction

The elements of the first column of Routh's array can be expressed in terms of a set of n determinants known as the *Hurwitz determinants*.[†] The requirement that, for stability, there must be no sign variations in the first column of Routh's array, is then equivalent to the requirement that the system parameters must satisfy a set of inequalities known as the *Hurwitz inequalities*. In this form the stability criterion is known as *Hurwitz's criterion*. Although the criteria of Routh and Hurwitz are equivalent, the Hurwitz inequalities are often simpler to construct and interpret than Routh's array, particularly when the coefficients in the characteristic polynomial are functions of several system parameters. In this chapter Hurwitz's criterion will be obtained first for real characteristic equations and then generalised so as to embrace equations having complex coefficients.

However, before deriving Hurwitz's criterion it is convenient at this stage to obtain a simple condition which is necessary but not sufficient for asymptotic stability: it will transpire that the Hurwitz inequalities can be greatly simplified for systems whose characteristic equations satisfy this necessary condition. If the general characteristic equation

$$F(s) = a_0 s^n + a_1 s^{n-1} + \ldots + a_{n-1} s + a_n = 0 \qquad (5.1)$$

has real coefficients, its complex roots will occur in conjugate pairs. Thus, if the equation has p real roots $\alpha_1, \alpha_2, \ldots, \alpha_p$, and q pairs of conjugate complex roots $\beta_1 \pm i\gamma_1, \beta_2 \pm i\gamma_2, \ldots, \beta_q \pm i\gamma_q$, the polynomial $F(s)$ can be written in the factored form

$$F(s) = a_0(s - \alpha_1) \ldots (s - \alpha_p)(s^2 - 2\beta_1 s + \beta_1^2 + \gamma_1^2) \ldots$$
$$(s^2 - 2\beta_q s + \beta_q^2 + \gamma_q^2). \qquad (5.2)$$

Now if the system governed by equation (5.1) is asymptotically stable, all the $\alpha_1, \ldots, \alpha_p$ and $\beta_1, \ldots, \beta_q$ will be negative and therefore all the coefficients in the factors of (5.2) will be positive. Consequently,

† A. Hurwitz, Über die Bedingungen, unter welchen eine Gleichung nur Wurzeln mit negativen reelen Teilen besitzt, *Math. Ann.*, **46**, 273, 1895.

when these factors are multiplied together to obtain equation (5.1), all the coefficients a_r ($1 \leqslant r \leqslant n$) thus produced will be non-zero and have the same sign as a_0. It follows that *if* a system having a real characteristic polynomial is asymptotically stable, *then* all the coefficients in the polynomial will be non-zero and of the same sign. It is important to note that this condition is necessary but not sufficient for asymptotic stability, i.e., if all the coefficients in equation (5.1) are real, non-zero and of the same sign, it cannot be deduced from this fact alone that the system is asymptotically stable.

These remarks can be illustrated by considering the following characteristic polynomials:

$$F_1(s) = s^6 + 2s^5 - 3s^4 + 5s^3 + s^2 + 7s + 6,$$
$$F_2(s) = 2s^5 + 2s^3 + 4s^2 + 3s + 9,$$
$$F_3(s) = s^4 + 5s^3 + 3s^2 + 2s + 3,$$
$$F_4(s) = 3s^5 + s^4 + 5s^3 + 4s^2 - 2s + (1 + 3i).$$

$F_1(s)$ represents a system which is not asymptotically stable since the coefficients are not all of the same sign; $F_2(s)$ also represents a system of this type because the coefficient of s^4 is zero; $F_3(s)$ represents a system whose stability cannot be decided on the basis of the necessary condition derived above since all the coefficients are positive; and the stability of the system governed by $F_4(s)$ is also indeterminate because of the presence of the complex coefficient.

5.2 Hurwitz's inequalities

In deriving the Hurwitz inequalities it is again convenient to write the real characteristic equation (5.1) in the alternative form

$$F(s) = A_0 s^n + B_0 s^{n-1} + A_1 s^{n-2} + B_1 s^{n-3} + \ldots = 0. \quad (5.3)$$

The $n \times n$ matrix

$$\mathbf{H}_n = \begin{bmatrix} B_0 & B_1 & B_2 & \cdots \\ A_0 & A_1 & A_2 & \cdots \\ 0 & B_0 & B_1 & \cdots \\ 0 & A_0 & A_1 & \cdots \\ 0 & 0 & B_0 & \cdots \\ 0 & 0 & A_0 & \cdots \\ \cdot & \cdot & \cdot & \cdots \\ \cdot & \cdot & \cdot & \cdots \end{bmatrix}, \quad (5.4)$$

known as the *Hurwitz matrix*, can then be formed from the coefficients in equation (5.3). In order to make $\mathbf{H}_n$ square and of the nth order, the coefficients are supplemented by zeros where necessary. For example, the Hurwitz matrix of the third-degree characteristic polynomial

$$F(s) = A_0 s^3 + B_0 s^2 + A_1 s + B_1$$

is

$$\mathbf{H}_3 = \begin{bmatrix} B_0 & B_1 & 0 \\ A_0 & A_1 & 0 \\ 0 & B_0 & B_1 \end{bmatrix}.$$

Since B_0 is the leading term in the second row of Routh's array (see (4.25b)), $B_0 \neq 0$ if the array is non-singular. In such circumstances the first, third, fifth, ..., rows of $\mathbf{H}_n$ may be multiplied by A_0/B_0 and then subtracted from the second, fourth, sixth, ..., rows of the matrix. The new matrix produced in this way has the form

$$\begin{bmatrix} B_0 & B_1 & B_2 & \cdots \\ 0 & C_0 & C_1 & \cdots \\ 0 & B_0 & B_1 & \cdots \\ 0 & 0 & C_0 & \cdots \\ 0 & 0 & B_0 & \cdots \\ 0 & 0 & 0 & \cdots \\ \cdot & \cdot & \cdot & \cdots \\ \cdot & \cdot & \cdot & \cdots \end{bmatrix}, \qquad (5.5)$$

where

$$C_0 = \frac{B_0 A_1 - A_0 B_1}{B_0}, \qquad C_1 = \frac{B_0 A_2 - A_0 B_2}{B_0}, \cdots$$

If these expressions are compared with those given in (4.21) it will be seen that C_0, C_1, C_2, ..., are the elements of the third row of Routh's array.

Now if Routh's array is non-singular, then $C_0 \neq 0$. In the non-singular case the second, fourth, sixth, ..., rows of the matrix (5.5) may therefore be multiplied by B_0/C_0 and then subtracted from the third, fifth, seventh, ..., rows to produce another new matrix. This has the form

$$\begin{bmatrix} B_0 & B_1 & B_2 & B_3 & \cdots \\ 0 & C_0 & C_1 & C_2 & \cdots \\ 0 & 0 & D_0 & D_1 & \cdots \\ 0 & 0 & C_0 & C_1 & \cdots \\ 0 & 0 & 0 & D_0 & \cdots \\ 0 & 0 & 0 & C_0 & \cdots \\ \cdot & \cdot & \cdot & \cdot & \cdots \\ \cdot & \cdot & \cdot & \cdot & \cdots \end{bmatrix}$$

where

$$D_0 = \frac{C_0 B_1 - B_0 C_1}{C_0}, \qquad D_1 = \frac{C_0 B_2 - B_0 C_2}{C_0}, \dots$$

If these expressions are compared with those given in (4.22) it will be seen that D_0, D_1, D_2, ..., are the elements of the fourth row of Routh's array.

If this procedure is repeated, an nth-order triangular matrix

$$\mathbf{R}_n = \begin{bmatrix} B_0 & B_1 & B_2 & B_3 & \cdots \\ 0 & C_0 & C_1 & C_2 & \cdots \\ 0 & 0 & D_0 & D_1 & \cdots \\ 0 & 0 & 0 & E_0 & \cdots \\ \cdot & \cdot & \cdot & \cdot & \cdots \\ \cdot & \cdot & \cdot & \cdot & \cdots \end{bmatrix}$$

is eventually produced. This is known as the *Routh matrix* of the real polynomial $F(s)$. It consists of all the rows of Routh's array (except the first) shifted to the right until each leading term lies on the leading diagonal of the matrix.

Now because of the method by which $\mathbf{R}_n$ was formed from $\mathbf{H}_n$, the theory of determinants indicates that the corresponding minors of $\mathbf{R}_n$ and $\mathbf{H}_n$ are equal. In particular, since the successive principal minors of $\mathbf{H}_n$ are

$$\Delta_1 = |B_0|, \tag{5.6a}$$

$$\Delta_2 = \begin{vmatrix} B_0 & B_1 \\ A_0 & A_1 \end{vmatrix}, \tag{5.6b}$$

$$\Delta_3 = \begin{vmatrix} B_0 & B_1 & B_2 \\ A_0 & A_1 & A_2 \\ 0 & B_0 & B_1 \end{vmatrix}, \tag{5.6c}$$

$$\cdot \quad \cdot \quad \cdot \quad \cdot \quad \cdot \quad \cdot$$

$$\Delta_n = \begin{vmatrix} B_0 & B_1 & B_2 & B_3 & \cdots \\ A_0 & A_1 & A_2 & A_3 & \cdots \\ 0 & B_0 & B_1 & B_2 & \cdots \\ 0 & A_0 & A_1 & A_2 & \cdots \\ \cdot & \cdot & \cdot & \cdot & \cdots \\ \cdot & \cdot & \cdot & \cdot & \cdots \end{vmatrix}, \tag{5.6n}$$

and the corresponding principal minors of $\mathbf{R}_n$ are

$$B_0, \, B_0 C_0, \, B_0 C_0 D_0, \dots,$$

it follows that

$$\Delta_1 = B_0, \qquad \Delta_2 = B_0 C_0, \qquad \Delta_3 = B_0 C_0 D_0, \qquad \dots \qquad (5.7)$$

Hence, the elements of the first column of Routh's array are given by

$$B_0 = \Delta_1, \qquad C_0 = \frac{\Delta_2}{\Delta_1}, \qquad D_0 = \frac{\Delta_3}{\Delta_2}, \dots \qquad (5.8)$$

The determinants $\Delta_1, \Delta_2, \dots, \Delta_n$ defined in equations (5.6) are called the *Hurwitz determinants* of the real polynominal $F(s)$.

It is evident from (5.7) that the Hurwitz determinants will be non-zero if and only if $B_0 \neq 0$, $C_0 \neq 0$, ... Thus, the non-singular case is characterised by the non-vanishing of all the Hurwitz determinants which is therefore a sufficient condition for the non-existence of imaginary characteristic roots. In the non-singular case it may therefore be deduced from (5.7) that the number of sign variations in the first column of Routh's array is

$$v(A_0, B_0, C_0, D_0, \dots) = v\left(A_0, \Delta_1, \frac{\Delta_2}{\Delta_1}, \frac{\Delta_3}{\Delta_2}, \dots, \frac{\Delta_n}{\Delta_{n-1}}\right).$$

Now if all the numbers in a given set are non-zero and of the same sign, the product of any even number of these numbers will be positive. Hence

$$v\left(A_0, \Delta_1, \frac{\Delta_2}{\Delta_1}, \frac{\Delta_3}{\Delta_2}, \dots, \frac{\Delta_n}{\Delta_{n-1}}\right) = 0$$

if and only if

$$A_0 \Delta_1 > 0, \qquad \Delta_2 > 0, \qquad A_0 \Delta_3 > 0, \qquad \Delta_4 > 0, \qquad \dots,$$

$$\left. \begin{array}{ll} A_0 \Delta_n > 0, & (n \text{ odd}), \\ \Delta_n > 0, & (n \text{ even}). \end{array} \right\} \qquad (5.9)$$

These inequalities are therefore necessary and sufficient conditions for asymptotic stability since they are equivalent to the requirements of Routh's criterion.

Since the characteristic equation can always be arranged so that $A_0 > 0$, the inequalities (5.9) can in practice be used in the simpler form

$$\Delta_1 > 0, \qquad \Delta_2 > 0, \qquad \Delta_3 > 0, \qquad \dots, \qquad \Delta_n > 0. \qquad (5.10)$$

These are known as the *Hurwitz inequalities* and express *Hurwitz's criterion* of asymptotic stability. It is evident that, in terms of the coefficients $a_0, a_1, \ldots, a_{n-1}, a_n$ which appear in the original characteristic equation (5.1), the Hurwitz determinants (5.6) are given by

$$
\Delta_r = \begin{vmatrix}
a_1 & a_3 & a_5 & \cdots & a_{2r-1} \\
a_0 & a_2 & a_4 & \cdots & a_{2r-2} \\
0 & a_1 & a_3 & \cdots & a_{2r-3} \\
0 & a_0 & a_2 & \cdots & a_{2r-4} \\
\cdot & \cdot & \cdot & \cdots & \cdot \\
\cdot & \cdot & \cdot & \cdots & \cdot \\
0 & 0 & 0 & \cdots & a_r
\end{vmatrix} \quad (r = 1, 2, \ldots, n), \qquad (5.11)
$$

where it is understood that any element a_k is zero if $k > n$.

As an illustration of the use of the Hurwitz inequalities, consider the characteristic equation

$$
F(s) = s^5 + 3s^4 + 2s^3 + s^2 + 4s + 7 = 0. \qquad (5.12)
$$

In this case,

$$
\Delta_1 = |3| = +3,
$$

$$
\Delta_2 = \begin{vmatrix} 3 & 1 \\ 1 & 2 \end{vmatrix} = +5,
$$

$$
\Delta_3 = \begin{vmatrix} 3 & 1 & 7 \\ 1 & 2 & 4 \\ 0 & 3 & 1 \end{vmatrix} = -10,
$$

$$
\Delta_4 = \begin{vmatrix} 3 & 1 & 7 & 0 \\ 1 & 2 & 4 & 0 \\ 0 & 3 & 1 & 7 \\ 0 & 1 & 2 & 4 \end{vmatrix} = -75,
$$

and

$$
\Delta_5 = \begin{vmatrix} 3 & 1 & 7 & 0 & 0 \\ 1 & 2 & 4 & 0 & 0 \\ 0 & 3 & 1 & 7 & 0 \\ 0 & 1 & 2 & 4 & 0 \\ 0 & 0 & 3 & 1 & 7 \end{vmatrix} = -525.
$$

Since $a_0 = A_0 = 1 > 0$ and Δ_3, Δ_4 and $\Delta_5 < 0$, the system governed by equation (5.12) is not asymptotically stable according to Hurwitz's criterion (5.10). Moreover, it follows from (5.8) that the first column of Routh's array is

$$
A_0 = +1, \quad B_0 = +3, \quad C_0 = +5/3, \quad D_0 = -10/5 = -2,
$$

$$
E_0 = -75/-10 = +15/2, \quad F_0 = -525/-75 = +7.
$$

Since there are two sign variations in this sequence of numbers, it follows from the properties of Routh's array that equation (5.12) has two roots with positive real parts. The system concerned is therefore unstable.

5.3   Criterion of Liénard-Chipart

It was shown in Section 5.1 that a necessary condition for all the roots of the real characteristic equation (5.1) to have negative real parts is that all the coefficients $a_0, a_1, \ldots, a_n$ are non-zero and have the same sign. If $F(s)$ is arranged so that $a_0 > 0$, this necessary condition becomes

$$a_0 > 0, \qquad a_1 > 0, \qquad a_2 > 0, \qquad \ldots, \qquad a_n > 0. \qquad (5.13)$$

Liénard and Chipart showed† that the Hurwitz inequalities (5.10) are not independent if the conditions (5.13) are satisfied. In fact, the Hurwitz determinants of odd order $(\Delta_1, \Delta_3, \ldots)$ are then positive if and only if those of even order $(\Delta_2, \Delta_4, \ldots)$ are positive. It follows that necessary and sufficient conditions for all the roots of equation (5.1) (with $a_0 > 0$) to lie in the left half of the s-plane can be expresssed in any of the following forms:

(i) $a_n > 0, a_{n-2} > 0, \ldots; \Delta_1 > 0, \Delta_3 > 0, \ldots:$ (5.14a)

(ii) $a_n > 0, a_{n-2} > 0, \ldots; \Delta_2 > 0, \Delta_4 > 0, \ldots:$ (5.14b)

(iii) $a_n > 0, a_{n-1} > 0, a_{n-3} > 0, \ldots; \Delta_1 > 0, \Delta_3 > 0, \ldots:$ (5.14c)

(iv) $a_n > 0, a_{n-1} > 0, a_{n-3} > 0, \ldots; \Delta_2 > 0, \Delta_4 > 0, \ldots.$ (5.14d)

These conditions constitute the *Lienard-Chipart criterion*.

This criterion is obviously simpler to apply than that of Hurwitz since it involves only about half the total number of Hurwitz determinants. For example, when $n = 3$ and $a_0 > 0$ the conditions (5.14b) indicate that it is necessary and sufficient for asymptotic stability that $a_3 > 0$, $a_1 > 0$ and $\Delta_2 = a_1 a_2 - a_0 a_3 > 0$. It follows that if all the coefficients in the cubic characteristic equation

$$F(s) = a_0 s^3 + a_1 s^2 + a_2 s + a_3 = 0$$

are positive, the condition for asymptotic stability is simply

$$a_1 a_2 - a_0 a_3 > 0.$$

Similar conditions can be obtained for characteristic equations of arbitrary degree having positive coefficients. These conditions are summarised in Table 5.1 when $n = 1, 2, 3, 4$, or 5. Note that when $n = 1$

† A. Liénard and M. H. Chipart, Sur la signe de la partie réelle des racines d'une equation algébrique, *J. Math. Pures Appl.*, **10**, 291, 1914.

TABLE 5.1 Necessary and sufficient conditions for asymptotic stability. (all coefficients in characteristic equation positive).

n	Stability conditions
1	—
2	—
3	$\Delta_2 = a_1 a_2 - a_0 a_3 > 0.$
4	$\Delta_3 = a_3(a_1 a_2 - a_0 a_3) - a_1^2 a_4 > 0.$
5	$\Delta_2 = a_1 a_2 - a_0 a_3 > 0,$ $\Delta_4 = (a_1 a_2 - a_0 a_3)(a_2 a_5 - a_3 a_4) - a_1 a_4(a_1 a_4 - a_0 a_5) > 0.$

or 2, no additional conditions are required: in these cases the conditions (5.13) are therefore sufficient as well as necessary for asymptotic stability.

The use of the stability conditions given in Table 5.1 can be illustrated by considering the characteristic equation

$$F(s) = s^4 + 4\mu p s^3 + p^2(1 + 4\mu^2)s^2 + 2\mu\Omega p^2 s + \mu^2\Omega^2 p^2 = 0.$$
$$(5.15)$$

This arises in the analysis of the effects of bearing characteristics on the stability of a gimbal-mounted gyroscope†. In equation (5.15), Ω is the angular velocity of the gyro rotor, p is the frequency of nutational oscillations of the rotor as a free body, and μ is a dimensionless function of the geometry of the main rotor bearings and the viscosity of the lubricant. Since all these parameters are positive quantities, all the coefficients in equation (5.15) are necessarily positive. The stability conditions given in Table 5.1 may therefore be used. In fact, since $a_0 = 1$, $a_1 = 4\mu p$, $a_2 = p^2(1 + 4\mu^2)$, $a_3 = 2\mu\Omega p^2$, and $a_4 = \mu^2\Omega^2 p^2$, the fourth entry in Table 5.1 indicates that a necessary and sufficient condition for asymptotic stability is

$$2\mu\Omega p^2\{4\mu p . p^2(1 + 4\mu^2) - 2\mu\Omega p^2\} - (4\mu p)^2 . \mu^2\Omega^2 p^2 > 0$$

which reduces to $p > \Omega/2$. The gyroscope will therefore be asymptotically stable if and only if the nutational frequency is greater than half the rotor speed.

As a second example, consider again the closed-loop control system whose block-diagram is shown in Fig. 3.10. The characteristic equation of this system is

$$\tau_1 \tau_2 s^3 + (\tau_1 + \tau_2)s^2 + s + \xi = 0, \qquad (5.16)$$

† J. M. Prentis, On the stability of a gimbal mounted gyroscope, *J.mech. Engng Sci.*, 3, 1, 1961.

where ξ is the open-loop gain, and τ_1 and τ_2 are time-constants associated with the forward path of the system. Since all these parameters are positive quantities, all the coefficients in equation (5.16) are positive. Table 5.1 may therefore be used and the third entry indicates that a necessary and sufficient condition for asymptotic stability is

$$(\tau_1 + \tau_2).1 - \tau_1\tau_2.\xi > 0,$$

since $a_0 = \tau_1\tau_2$, $a_1 = (\tau_1 + \tau_2)$, $a_2 = 1$ and $a_3 = \xi$ in the present case. This condition reduces to

$$\xi < \frac{(\tau_1 + \tau_2)}{\tau_1\tau_2}$$

which agrees with that obtained by Nyquist's criterion in Chapter 3.

5.4 Stability boundaries

It is often necessary to determine the conditions under which a system is on a boundary between stable and unstable behaviour. In the case of the real characteristic equation (5.1), there are three ways in which a transition from stability to instability can occur:

(i) A real root can cross from the left to the right half of the s-plane by moving along the real axis and passing through the origin.

(ii) A root can cross from the left to the right half-plane as a result of its real part jumping from $-\infty$ to $+\infty$.

(iii) A pair of conjugate complex roots having negative real parts can become conjugate imaginary roots and then move into the right half-plane as conjugate complex roots having positive real parts.

A system is on a stability boundary of the first kind if $a_n = 0$ and all the remaining stability conditions are satisfied; for when $a_n = 0$, $s = 0$ is obviously a root of equation (5.1). A system is on a stability boundary of the second kind if $a_0 = 0$ and all the remaining stability conditions are satisfied; for when $a_0 \to 0$, it is evident that one root of equation (5.1) tends to infinity. It can be shown that a system is on a stability boundary of the third kind if $\Delta_{n-1} = 0$ (where Δ_{n-1} is the penultimate Hurwitz determinant) and all the remaining stability conditions are satisfied.

The last result can be deduced from a theorem obtained by Orlando†. This states that

$$\Delta_{n-1} = (-1)^{\frac{n(n-1)}{2}} a_0^{n-1} \prod_{j<k}^{1,\cdots,n} (s_j + s_k) \quad (n \geqslant 2), \quad (5.17)$$

† L. Orlando, Sul problema di Hurwitz relative alle parti realli delle radici di un'equazione algebrica, *Math.Ann.*, **71**, 233, 1911.

where the s_r ($r = 1, 2, \ldots, n$) are the roots of equation (5.1), and the Π term denotes the product of these roots taken in pairs. For example, when $n = 3$ equation (5.17) becomes

$$\Delta_2 = (-1)^3 a_0^2 (s_1 + s_2)(s_2 + s_3)(s_1 + s_3).$$

Orlando's theorem implies that $\Delta_{n-1} = 0$ if and only if the characteristic equation (5.1) has at least one pair of roots whose sum is zero. Now if all the stability conditions except that involving Δ_{n-1} are satisfied. it may be inferred that equation (5.1) has no roots with positive real parts and no zero roots. The only possible roots whose sum can be zero are therefore pairs of conjugate imaginary roots of the type $s = \pm i\omega$. It follows that if $\Delta_{n-1} = 0$ and all the remaining stability conditions are satisfied, equation (5.1) has at least one pair of conjugate imaginary roots and the system is on a stability boundary of the third kind.

As an example of the use of Orlando's theorem consider the characteristic equation

$$F(s) = s^3 + 5s^2 + 6s + \xi = 0 \qquad (5.18)$$

in which ξ is a real parameter. In this case the penultimate Hurwitz determinant is

$$\Delta_2 = \begin{vmatrix} 5 & \xi \\ 1 & 6 \end{vmatrix} = 30 - \xi$$

which clearly vanishes when $\xi = 30$. Since all the coefficients in equation (5.18) are then positive, it may be deduced, that there are two conjugate imaginary roots and one negative real root when $\xi = 30$. In fact, putting $s = i\omega$ in equation (5.18) when $\xi = 30$ yields

$$F(i\omega) = (-5\omega^2 + 30) + i(-\omega^3 + 6\omega) = 0$$

which implies that $\omega = \pm\sqrt{6}$. The conjugate imaginary roots are consequently $s = \pm i\sqrt{6}$, and the remaining real root is easily found to be $s = -5$. This confirms that the system governed by equation (5.18) is on a stability boundary of the third kind when $\xi = 30$.

Note that when $\xi = 0$, the remaining coefficients in equation (5.18) are positive and also $\Delta_2 = 30 > 0$. According to the reasoning given at the beginning of this section, the system governed by equation (5.18) is therefore on a stability boundary of the first kind when $\xi = 0$. This conclusion can be verified by noting that the roots of (5.18) are $s = 0$, -2, -3 when $\xi = 0$.

5.5 Characteristic equations having complex coefficients

In Section 4.7 it was shown that the mathematical results which form the basis of Routh's criterion can be used to investigate the stability of systems governed by characteristic equations having complex coefficients. It can also be shown that the criterion of Hurwitz can be similarly extended.

If $F(s)$ is a characteristic polynomial having complex coefficients let

$$F(i\omega) = B_0\omega^n + B_1\omega^{n-1} + \ldots + B_n$$
$$+ i(A_0\omega^n + A_1\omega^{n-1} + \ldots + A_n), \quad (5.19)$$

where the A_r and B_r are real numbers. The stability of the system governed by $F(s)$ can be characterised by the values of the n determinants $V_2, V_4, \ldots, V_{2n}$ defined by

$$V_{2r} = \begin{vmatrix} A_0 & A_1 & \ldots & A_{2r-1} \\ B_0 & B_1 & \ldots & B_{2r-1} \\ 0 & A_0 & \ldots & A_{2r-2} \\ 0 & B_0 & \ldots & B_{2r-2} \\ \cdot & \cdot & \ldots & \cdot \\ \cdot & \cdot & \ldots & \cdot \end{vmatrix} \quad (r = 1, 2, \ldots, n), \quad (5.20)$$

where A_k and B_k are zero if $k > n$, and V_{2r} is of the 2rth order. In fact, it can be shown† that all the zeros of $F(s)$ have negative real parts if

$$V_2 > 0, \quad V_4 > 0, \quad \ldots, \quad V_{2n} > 0. \quad (5.21)$$

Further, if some of these inequalities are not satisfied but all of the V_{2r} are non-zero, it can also be shown that the number of zeros of $F(s)$ lying in the right half of the s-plane is equal to the number of sign variations in the sequence 1, $V_2, V_4, \ldots, V_{2n}$.

The stability conditions (5.21) are known as the *generalised Hurwitz inequalities*. It can easily be verified that they reduce to the ordinary Hurwitz inequalities (5.10) when the polynomial $F(s)$ has real coefficients.

The use of the generalised Hurwitz inequalities can be illustrated by considering the complex characteristic equation

$$F(s) = s^2 + 2v\omega_n s + (\omega_n^2 - 2iv\omega_n\Omega) = 0. \quad (5.22)$$

† See F. R. Gantmacher, *Applications of the theory of matrices*, p. 295, Interscience, New York, 1959.

This equation arises in the theory of shaft whirling and was analysed in Section 4.7 by means of Sturm's theorem. In this case,

$$F(i\omega) = (-\omega^2 + \omega_n^2) + i(2v\omega_n\omega - 2v\omega_n\Omega)$$

so that, in the notation of equation (5.19), $A_0 = 0$, $A_1 = 2v\omega_n$, $A_2 = -2v\omega_n\Omega$, $B_0 = -1$, $B_1 = 0$, and $B_2 = \omega_n^2$. The determinants $\mathbf{V}_2$ and $\mathbf{V}_4$ defined by (5.20) are accordingly

$$\mathbf{V}_2 = \begin{vmatrix} 0 & 2v\omega_n \\ -1 & 0 \end{vmatrix} = 2v\omega_n$$

and

$$\mathbf{V}_4 = \begin{vmatrix} 0 & 2v\omega_n & -2v\omega_n\Omega & 0 \\ -1 & 0 & \omega_n^2 & 0 \\ 0 & 0 & 2v\omega_n & -2v\omega_n\Omega \\ 0 & -1 & 0 & \omega_n^2 \end{vmatrix} = 4v^2\omega_n^2(\omega_n^2 - \Omega^2).$$

Now $\mathbf{V}_2$ is always positive, since it is assumed that $v > 0$ and $\omega_n > 0$. But $\mathbf{V}_4$ is positive only if $\Omega < \omega_n$, which is therefore the condition for asymptotic stability according to the generalised Hurwitz inequalities (5.21). If $\Omega > \omega_n$, there is one sign variation in the sequence 1, $\mathbf{V}_2$, $\mathbf{V}_4$, and therefore one characteristic root in the right half of the s-plane. These results agree with those previously obtained on the basis of Sturm's theorem.

5.6 Absolute and relative stability margins

Although the transient response of an asymptotically stable linear system dies away as $t \to \infty$, such a response may still be unsatisfactory from a practical viewpoint. For example, the transient response may decay too slowly or be poorly damped and therefore too oscillatory. These considerations are of particular importance in the design of automatic control systems.

The occurrence of a slow transient can be prevented by requiring that all the characteristic roots lie to the left of a specified line $s = -\delta(\delta > 0)$ which is parallel to the imaginary axis in the s-plane. If all the roots lie in such a region (shown cross-hatched in Fig. 5.1), it follows from the general expressions obtained in Chapter 2 for the transient response components that the corresponding transient response will decay at least as rapidly as $e^{-\delta t}$. The system is then said to possess an *absolute stability margin* δ.

It is a straightforward matter to test a system for absolute stability

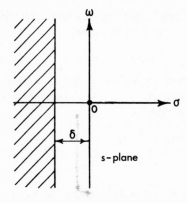

Fig. 5.1. Region of absolute stability in the s-plane.

by means of any of the standard stability criteria. It is only necessary to introduce a new variable S defined by $S = s + \delta$ and then determine whether any of the roots of the modified characteristic equation lie in the right half of the S-plane. This procedure can be made systematic by using the techniques for investigating stability boundaries described in Section 5.4. Thus, if the characteristic equation of an asymptotically stable linear system has the form

$$F(s) = a_0 s^n + a_1 s^{n-1} + \ldots + a_{n-1} s + a_n = 0, \qquad (5.23)$$

where all the a_r are real and positive, the modified characteristic equation obtained by putting $s = S - \delta$ will have the form

$$F(S - \delta) = b_0 S^n + b_1 S^{n-1} + \ldots + b_{n-1} S + b_n = 0. \qquad (5.24)$$

The b_r $(1 \leqslant r \leqslant n)$ will in general be functions of δ, but equation (5.24) can always be arranged so that b_0 is independent of δ. The Hurwitz determinants $\Delta_1, \Delta_2, \ldots, \Delta_n$ formed from the b_r will be functions of δ which are all positive when $\delta = 0$ since equation (5.23) is assumed to represent an asymptotically stable system. Similarly, all the b_r will be positive when $\delta = 0$.

If the value of δ is gradually increased from zero, eventually one of the Hurwitz determinants or one of the b_r will vanish. Now since b_0 is assumed to be independent of δ, the first coefficient to vanish will be b_n (corresponding to the existence of a real root at the origin of the S-plane). On the other hand, it follows from Orlando's theorem that the first Hurwitz determinant to vanish will be Δ_{n-1} (corresponding to the existence of a pair of conjugate roots on the imaginary axis of the S-plane). In general, the values of δ for which b_n and Δ_{n-1} first vanish will be different. If this is the case and the smaller of the two values is $\bar{\delta}$, the foregoing considerations indicate that all the roots of equation

(5.23) must lie on or to the left of the line $s = -\tilde{\delta}$ in the s-plane. The value of $\tilde{\delta}$ can be conveniently obtained by plotting b_n and Δ_{n-1} as functions of δ and observing the smaller of the values of δ at which the two curves first cross the δ-axis.

This technique can be illustrated by investigating the absolute stability of a system whose characteristic equation is

$$F(s) = s^3 + 4s^2 + 4s + 3 = 0. \qquad (5.25)$$

This system is asymptotically stable since all the coefficients in equation (5.25) are positive and $\Delta_2 = 13 > 0$. If the variable $S = s + \delta$ is introduced, equation (5.25) becomes

$$F(S - \delta) = S^3 + (4 - 3\delta)S^2 + (4 - 8\delta + 3\delta^2)S$$
$$+ (3 - 4\delta + 4\delta^2 - \delta^3) = 0.$$

It is evident that

$$b_3(\delta) = 3 - 4\delta + 4\delta^2 - \delta^3,$$

and it may be deduced that

$$\Delta_2(\delta) = 13 - 40\delta + 32\delta^2 - 8\delta^3.$$

These quantities are plotted as functions of δ in Fig. 5.2. It is clear that $b_3(\delta) > 0$ when $0 < \delta < 3$, and also that $\Delta_2(\delta) > 0$ when $0 < \delta < \frac{1}{2}$. It follows that $\tilde{\delta} = \frac{1}{2}$ and consequently that equation (5.25) has two conjugate complex roots with real parts equal to $-\frac{1}{2}$, but no roots with real parts greater than $-\frac{1}{2}$. The transient response of the system governed by equation (5.25) will therefore decay at least as rapidly as $e^{-t/2}$.

The transient response of a system possessing a reasonable margin of absolute stability may nevertheless be so poorly damped that it performs a large number of oscillatory cycles before effectively coming to rest. The occurrence

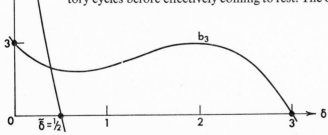

Fig. 5.2. Determination of absolute stability margin of system governed by equation 5.25.

of a poorly damped transient of this type can be prevented by insisting that all the characteristic roots lie in a region of the s-plane like that shown in Fig. 5.3. A system having this property is said to possess a *relative stability margin*, θ; for it follows from the discussion of the

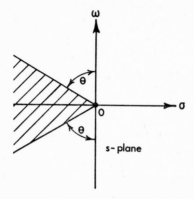

Fig. 5.3. Region of relative stability in the s-plane.

second-order system given in Section 2.3 that all pairs of conjugate complex roots located in the cross-hatched region of Fig. 5.3 will give rise to components of transient response whose dimensionless damping parameters v are such that $v \geqslant \sin \theta$. This implies that the greater the margin of relative stability, the fewer the number of cycles required for the amplitude of an oscillatory component of transient response to decay to a specified level from an initial value.

The relative stability of a linear system can be investigated by means of the generalised Hurwitz inequalities given in Section 5.5. However,

Fig. 5.4. Relationship between the s-plane and the S-plane.

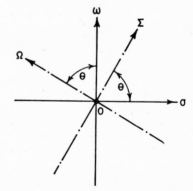

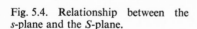

it is first necessary to introduce a new variable S defined by $S = e^{-i\theta}s$. The resulting relationship between the s-plane and the S-plane is shown in Fig. 5.4, where the s-plane is defined by the σ-, ω-axes and the S-

plane by the Σ-, Ω-axes. If the new variable S is introduced into the real characteristic equation (5.23), the resulting equation has the form

$$F(e^{i\theta}S) \equiv G(S) = a_0(\cos n\theta + i \sin n\theta)S^n$$

$$+ a_1(\cos \overline{n-1}\theta + i \sin \overline{n-1}\theta)S^{n-1}$$

$$+ \ldots \ldots \ldots \ldots$$

$$+ a_{n-1}(\cos \theta + i \sin \theta)S$$

$$+ a_n = 0, \tag{5.26}$$

since $e^{in\theta} \equiv \cos n\theta + i \sin n\theta$.

If the system governed by equation (5.23) is asymptotically stable, then no characteristic roots lie in the right half of the s-plane or on the imaginary axis. Hence, if k roots of equation (5.26) lie in the right half of the S-plane, it follows that k roots of equation (5.23) must be located in the sector of the s-plane bounded by the positive ω- and positive Ω-axes shown in Fig. 5.4. Since equation (5.23) is assumed to have real coefficients, its complex roots occur in conjugate pairs so that k roots must also lie in the sector of the s-plane bounded by the negative ω-axis and the mirror image of the positive Ω-axis in the σ-axis. If, for a given value of θ, it is found that $k = 0$, it may be concluded that no roots lie in these sectors and consequently that all oscillatory components of transient response have damping parameters not less than $\sin \theta$. The value of k is equal to the number of roots of equation (5.26) having positive real parts and can therefore be found by using the generalised Hurwitz criterion given in the last section.

As a first illustrative example of this method of investigating relative stability, consider the simple characteristic equation

$$F(s) = s^2 + 2s + 2 = 0. \tag{5.27}$$

If the variable $S = e^{-i\theta}s$ is introduced, this equation becomes

$$F(e^{i\theta}S) \equiv G(S) = (\cos 2\theta + i \sin 2\theta)S^2 + $$
$$2(\cos \theta + i \sin \theta)S + 2 = 0. \tag{5.28}$$

In order to use the generalised Hurwitz criterion it is necessary to evaluate $G(S)$ on the imaginary axis in the S-plane. This gives

$$G(i\Omega) = (-\cos 2\theta)\Omega^2 + (-2 \sin \theta)\Omega + 2$$
$$+ i\{(-\sin 2\theta)\Omega^2 + (2 \cos \theta)\Omega\}.$$

In the notation of equation (5.19) and (5.20) it follows that

$$\mathbf{V}_2 = \begin{vmatrix} -\sin 2\theta & 2\cos\theta \\ -\cos 2\theta & -2\sin\theta \end{vmatrix} = 2\cos\theta$$

and

$$\mathbf{V}_4 = \begin{vmatrix} -\sin 2\theta & 2\cos\theta & 0 & 0 \\ -\cos 2\theta & -2\sin\theta & 2 & 0 \\ 0 & -\sin 2\theta & 2\cos\theta & 0 \\ 0 & -\cos 2\theta & -2\sin\theta & 2 \end{vmatrix} = 8\cos^2\theta\cos 2\theta.$$

Now $\mathbf{V}_2 = +2$ and $\mathbf{V}_4 = +8$ when $\theta = 0$, confirming that equation (5.27) represents an asymptotically stable system. Furthermore, it is clear that $\mathbf{V}_2 > 0$ for all values of θ in the range $0 < \theta < 90°$. But although $\mathbf{V}_4 > 0$ when $0 < \theta < 45°$, it is evident that $\mathbf{V}_4 < 0$ when $45° < \theta < 90°$. This result implies that the roots of equation (5.27) lie in the domain of the s-plane shown in Fig. 5.3 only when $0 < \theta < 45°$. It follows that equation (5.27) has conjugate complex roots which will give rise to an oscillatory transient response whose damping parameter is $\sin 45° = 1/\sqrt{2}$.

Since (5.27) is a quadratic equation, these results can be obtained much more readily by direct calculation (in fact, the roots of (5.27) are $-1 \pm i$). However, the last example illustrates a general procedure which can be used equally in non-trivial cases where the characteristic roots are not so easily calculable. Consider, for example, the cubic characteristic equation (5.25) whose absolute stability was investigated at the beginning of this section. In this case, the two substitutions $S = e^{-i\theta}s$ and $S = i\Omega$ yield

$$G(i\Omega) = (\sin 3\theta)\Omega^3 + (-4\cos 2\theta)\Omega^2 + (-4\sin\theta)\Omega + 3 \\ + i\{(-\cos 3\theta)\Omega^3 + (-4\sin 2\theta)\Omega^2 + (4\cos\theta)\Omega\}$$

from which it may be deduced that the determinants (5.20) are

$$\mathbf{V}_2 = \begin{vmatrix} -\cos 3\theta & -4\sin 2\theta \\ \sin 3\theta & -4\cos 2\theta \end{vmatrix} = 4\cos\theta,$$

$$\mathbf{V}_4 = \begin{vmatrix} -\cos 3\theta & -4\sin 2\theta & 4\cos\theta & 0 \\ \sin 3\theta & -4\cos 2\theta & -4\sin\theta & 3 \\ 0 & -\cos 3\theta & -4\sin 2\theta & 4\cos\theta \\ 0 & \sin 3\theta & -4\cos 2\theta & -4\sin\theta \end{vmatrix}$$

$$= 24 + 26\cos 2\theta + 2\cos 4\theta,$$

and

$$\mathbf{V}_6 = \begin{vmatrix} -\cos3\theta & -4\sin2\theta & 4\cos\theta & 0 & 0 & 0 \\ \sin3\theta & -4\cos2\theta & -4\sin\theta & 3 & 0 & 0 \\ 0 & -\cos3\theta & -4\sin2\theta & 4\cos\theta & 0 & 0 \\ 0 & \sin3\theta & -4\cos2\theta & -4\sin\theta & 3 & 0 \\ 0 & 0 & -\cos3\theta & -4\sin2\theta & 4\cos\theta & 0 \\ 0 & 0 & \sin3\theta & -4\cos2\theta & -4\sin\theta & 3 \end{vmatrix}$$

$$= 84\cos\theta + \tfrac{1329}{4}\cos3\theta + 120\cos5\theta - 36\cos7\theta + \tfrac{27}{4}\cos9\theta.$$

Now $\mathbf{V}_2 = +4$, $\mathbf{V}_4 = +52$ and $\mathbf{V}_6 = +507$ when $\theta = 0$, confirming that equation (5.25) represents an asymptotically stable system. The determinants $\mathbf{V}_2$ and $\mathbf{V}_4$ are also positive for all values of θ in the range $0 < \theta < 90°$. However, $\mathbf{V}_6$ is positive when $0 < \theta < 30°$ but negative when $30° < \theta < 90°$. It may therefore be concluded that the roots of equation (5.25) lie in the domain of the s-plane shown in Fig. 5.3 only when $0 < \theta < 30°$. This result implies that equation (5.25) has a pair of conjugate complex roots which will give rise to a component of oscillatory transient response whose damping parameter is $\sin 30° = \tfrac{1}{2}$. Note that the combined results of the analyses of the absolute and relative stability of the system governed by equation (5.25) indicate that the characteristic roots lie within or on the boundary of the cross-hatched region of the s-plane shown in Fig. 5.5.

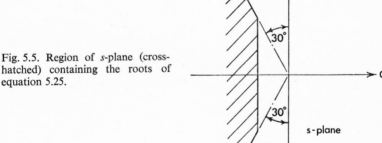

Fig. 5.5. Region of s-plane (cross-hatched) containing the roots of equation 5.25.

In both the foregoing investigations of relative stability, it will be noted that the first determinant to change sign is $\mathbf{V}_{2n}$. A generalised version of Orlando's theorem for equations having complex coefficients ensures that this is always the case†. Thus, if V_{2n} is plotted as a function of θ for a system which is known to be asymptotically stable, the first value of θ ($< 90°$) at which V_{2n} crosses the θ-axis gives the relative stability margin of the system under investigation.

Problems

1. The directional stability of an automobile may be analysed approximately by regarding the vehicle as a rigid horizontal rectangular frame having a wheel rigidly mounted at each corner. The characteristic equation of such a system has the form‡

$$s^2 + \frac{2}{mV}\left[K_1\left(1 + \frac{a_1^2}{\rho^2}\right) + K_2\left(1 + \frac{a_2^2}{\rho^2}\right)\right]s$$

$$+ \left[\frac{4K_1K_2(a_1 + a_2)^2}{m^2\rho^2v^2} - \frac{2(K_1a_1 - K_2a_2)}{m\rho^2}\right] = 0,$$

where m is the mass of the entire frame, ρ is its radius of gyration about a vertical axis through the centre of gravity G, a_1 and a_2 are respectively the distances of the front and back axles from G, V is the forward speed of the vehicle, and K_1 and K_2 are respectively the coefficients of transverse creep for the front and back wheels. Show that this system will be asymptotically stable at all speeds if $K_1a_1 \leqslant K_2a_2$, but will otherwise become unstable when

$$V^2 > \frac{2K_1K_2(a_1 + a_2)^2}{m(K_1a_1 - K_2a_2)}.$$

It may be assumed that $K_1, K_2 > 0$.

2. A simple model for investigating the instability of suspension bridges in winds§ consists of an initially horizontal plate suspended from four identical vertical springs of total stiffness k: the plate is of depth $2l$ in the direction of the horizontal wind, of mass m, and of moment of inertia I about its horizontal transverse axis. If the rotation of the plate about its transverse axis is θ, and the vertical displacement of its centre of gravity is x, then the linearised equations of motion of the plate can be written in the form

$$m\frac{d^2x}{dt^2} + kx = L,$$

$$I\frac{d^2\theta}{dt^2} + kl^2\theta = \frac{Ll}{2},$$

† See J. F. Koenig, On the zeros of polynomials and the degree of stability of linear systems, *J. appl. Phys.*, **24**, 476, 1953.
‡ Y. Rocard, *Dynamic instability*, p. 72, Crosby Lockwood, 1957.
§ Y. Rocard, op. cit., p. 145.

where L is the aerodynamic lift given by

$$L = \lambda\left(V^2\theta - V\frac{dx}{dt}\right),$$

V is the speed of the wind, and λ is the lift coefficient. Show that, if $I > ml^2$, the plate will be asymptotically stable only when

$$V^2 < 2kl/\lambda.$$

Use Orlando's theorem to discuss the behaviour of the plate if $V^2 < 2kl/\lambda$ but $I = ml^2$.

3. The roll-stabilisation system of an aircraft† consists of a closed-loop control system which automatically develops a restoring torque if the aircraft rolls from a desired angular position ϕ. The dynamics of the aircraft may be approximately described by the equation

$$I\frac{d^2\theta}{dt^2} = k\alpha \quad (k > 0),$$

where θ is the angle of roll, I is the moment of inertia of the aircraft about its longitudinal axis, and $k\alpha$ is the torque produced by a deflection α of the ailerons. The servo-motor which operates the ailerons is governed by an equation of the form

$$T\frac{d\alpha}{dt} + \alpha = u,$$

and the controller which generates the signal u behaves in accordance with the equation

$$u = \varepsilon + aT\frac{d\varepsilon}{dt},$$

where $\varepsilon = \phi - \theta$, and a and T are positive parameters. Derive the differential equation relating θ to ϕ, and hence show that the system will be asymptotically stable if and only if $a > 1$.

4. A two-degree of-freedom representation of the nose-wheel assembly of an aircraft‡ consists of a rigid horizontal swiveling structure S_1, which carries a wheel at one end P and is hinged to a flexible non-swiveling structure S_2 at the other end Q. S_1 is of mass m_1, and of moment of inertia I_1 about a vertical axis through its centre of gravity G, where $PG = a$, $GQ = b$, and $PQ = l$. S_2 consists of a particle

† J-C. Gille, M. J. Pelegrin, P. Decaulne, *Feedback control systems*, p. 255, McGraw-Hill, 1959.

‡ W. J. Moreland, Landing-gear vibration, *A. F. Technical Report 6590*, Wright Air Development Center, 1951.

of mass m_2 which is concentrated at Q and is coupled to a massive frame (representing the fuselage of the aircraft) by means of a horizontal transverse spring of stiffness k_2: the frame moves with a constant speed V in a fixed direction which coincides with that of PQ when the system is not vibrating. However, if vibrations occur such that PQ makes a small angle θ with the direction of V, and m_2 suffers a small transverse displacement x from its equilibrium position, then the equations governing the behaviour of the system are

$$
\left.
\begin{aligned}
\frac{dx}{dt} &= -l\frac{d\theta}{dt} - V\theta, \\[2mm]
I_1\frac{d^2\theta}{dt^2} &= \left(k_2x + m_2\frac{d^2x}{dt^2}\right)l + \left(\frac{d^2x}{dt^2} + b\frac{d^2\theta}{dt^2}\right)am_1 - c\frac{d\theta}{dt},
\end{aligned}
\right\}
$$

where c is the torsional viscous damping coefficient for swiveling at Q. Show that this system will be asymptotically stable if and only if

$$
c > \frac{V}{l}(I_1 - m_1ab).
$$

If the damping coefficient is reduced until the system becomes marginally stable, show that steady shimmying vibrations can then occur with a circular frequency

$$
\left[\frac{k_2l^2}{I_1 + m_1a^2 + m_2l^2}\right]^{\frac{1}{2}}.
$$

5. Investigate the margins of absolute and relative stability of systems governed by the following characteristic equations:

(a) $s^3 + 2s^2 + 2s + 3 = 0$.
(b) $s^4 + 2s^3 + 3s^2 + s + 1 = 0$.

6. Discuss the behaviour of the roots of the following equations as the value of the real parameter ξ increases from 0 to $+\infty$:

(a) $s^3 + 4s^2 + 2s + 1 - \xi = 0$.
(b) $(2 - \xi)s^3 + 3s^2 + 6s + 1 = 0$.
(c) $(3 - \xi)s^3 + 2s^2 + (5 - 2\xi)s + 2 = 0$.

7. The behaviour of a certain system† subjected to gyroscopic forces is governed by the equations

$$
\left.
\begin{aligned}
(D^2 + p_1D + q_1)x_1(t) - (p_2D + q_2)x_2(t) &= 0, \\
(p_2D + q_2)x_1(t) + (D^2 + p_1D + q_1)x_2(t) &= 0,
\end{aligned}
\right\}
$$

† H. Bateman, The control of an elastic fluid, *Bull. Am. math. Soc.* **51**, 601, 1945.

where $D \equiv d/dt$ and the p_r and q_r are positive constants. Show that the characteristic equation of this system can be expressed in the form

$$s^2 + (p_1 + ip_2)s + q_1 + iq_2 = 0$$

and hence determine necessary and sufficient conditions for asymptotic stability.

Chapter 6

ROOT-LOCI

6.1 Introduction

Algebraic criteria such as those of Routh and Hurwitz sometimes lead to stability conditions whose interpretation is rather difficult, particularly when a number of system parameters are involved. In order to facilitate analysis in such cases, alternative methods have been developed which display in graphical form the dependence of stability on the values of system parameters.

Two principal methods of this type are available:

(i) Trajectories can be plotted showing the variation of the characteristic roots in the s-plane as the system parameters vary: these trajectories are known as *root-loci*.

(ii) The regions of parameter space corresponding to stable behaviour, or to various margins of absolute or relative stability, can be constructed: this is known as the *D-partition* of the parameter space.

In principle, these two methods are equivalent and merely present the same information in different forms. However, each has its own limitations which in certain circumstances make the other preferable. For example, root-loci can show the effect of varying only one parameter at a time, whilst the method of *D*-partition can easily cope with up to two system parameters. However, when only one parameter is involved, a root-locus chart provides a complete picture of stability (including absolute and relative stability margins) in a single diagram, whereas a number of *D*-partitions of parameter space are necessary to obtain the same information. The two methods are thus complementary. Rules for constructing root-loci are given in this chapter, and the method of *D*-partition is described in the next.

6.2 Root-loci

The transient response characteristics of certain systems are largely determined by the value of one parameter: thus, for example, in closed-loop control systems the open-loop gain has a crucial effect on stability.

Root-loci† provide a very convenient means of analysing the stability of such systems in cases where the system parameter occurs linearly in the characteristic equation, i.e., when this equation has the form

$$F(s) = P(s) + \xi Q(s) = 0. \tag{6.1}$$

In (6.1), ξ is a positive or negative real parameter, and $P(s)$ and $Q(s)$ are real polynomials in s. By dividing throughout by $P(s)$, equation (6.1) can be written in the form

$$1 + \xi H(s) = 0, \tag{6.2}$$

where

$$H(s) = \frac{Q(s)}{P(s)}. \tag{6.3}$$

As was shown in Section 3.4, characteristic equations of the form (6.2) occur in the analysis of closed-loop control systems where $\xi H(s) = G(s)$ is then the open-loop transfer function and ξ is the open-loop gain. In such applications, ξ is restricted to positive values.

It is evident from equation (6.1) that, for any value of ξ, the characteristic roots are function of the zeros of $P(s)$ and $Q(s)$, the last quantities being respectively the poles and zeros of the function

$$H(s) = Q(s)/P(s).$$

As ξ varies, the characteristic roots move about in the s-plane and their trajectories constitute the *root-loci*. If the characteristic equation can be solved for its roots as explicit functions of ξ, the root-loci can easily be plotted and provide a useful summary of the dependence of system stability on ξ (the loci for the first- and second-order systems shown in Figs. 2.5 and 2.11 were plotted in this way). However, it is possible to determine the salient features of root-loci by applying simple rules which obviate the necessity of solving the characteristic equation: the method thus becomes applicable to quite complicated systems.

Before deriving these rules, it is necessary to obtain the conditions that must be satisfied if a point in the s-plane is to lie on a root-locus. These conditions can be obtained by writing equation (6.2) in the form

$$\xi H(s) = -1 = \exp\{i(2k + 1)\pi\}, \tag{6.4}$$

where k is any integer. It follows that

$$|\xi H(s)| = 1 \tag{6.5a}$$

and

$$\arg \xi H(s) = (2k + 1)\pi \tag{6.5b}$$

on a root-locus.

† W. R. Evans, Graphical analysis of Control Systems, *Trans. Am. Inst. elect Engng*, **67**, 547, 1948.

Now it is always possible to choose ξ in equation (6.2) in such a way that $H(s)$ has the factored form†

$$H(s) = \frac{(s - z_1)(s - z_2) \ldots (s - z_m)}{(s - p_1)(s - p_2) \ldots (s - p_n)} = \frac{\prod\limits_{j=1}^{m} (s - z_j)}{\prod\limits_{j=1}^{n} (s - p_j)},$$

where the p_j and z_j are respectively the poles and zeros of $H(s)$. If $H(s)$ has this form, the conditions (6.5) imply that

$$|\xi| = \frac{\prod\limits_{j=1}^{n} |s - p_j|}{\prod\limits_{j=1}^{m} |s - z_j|} \tag{6.6a}$$

and

$$\sum_{j=1}^{m} \arg (s - z_j) - \sum_{j=1}^{n} \arg (s - p_j) = \left. \begin{array}{l} (2k + 1)\pi, \quad (\xi > 0), \\ 2k\pi, \quad (\xi < 0). \end{array} \right\} \tag{6.6b}$$

The factor $(s - z_j)$ can be represented by the vector drawn from the zero z_j to the point s. Similarly, $(s - p_j)$ can be represented by the vector drawn from the pole p_j to s. Equations (6.6) may therefore be interpreted in terms of the vectors obtained by joining all the poles and zeros of $H(s)$ to an arbitrary point s. If the sum of the arguments of all the vectors emanating from the poles is subtracted from the corresponding sum for the zeros, equation (6.6b) states that the point s is on a root-locus only if this difference is equal to an integral multiple of π (odd multiples corresponding to $\xi > 0$, and even multiples to $\xi < 0$). The value of $|\xi|$ corresponding to any point on the root-loci determined in this way can be found in accordance with equation (6.6a) by dividing the product of the lengths of all the vectors emanating from the poles by the corresponding product for the zeros: the sign of ξ can then be found by noting which of equations (6.6b) is satisfied at the point under consideration. These results form the basis of the following rules for constructing root-loci.

6.3 Rules for constructing root-loci

(i) NUMBER OF LOCI

The number of root-loci is equal to the degree of the characteristic equation.

† The numerator and denominator of $H(s)$ are then both monic polynomials (i.e., the coefficient of the highest power of s is unity in both cases). It can be assumed without loss of generality that $n \geqslant m$.

This is obvious since the number of characteristic roots is equal to the degree of the characteristic equation, and each root has its own locus.

(ii) SYMMETRY OF LOCI

The root-loci for a real characteristic equation are symmetrical with respect to the real axis.

This follows from the fact that the complex roots of a real characteristic equation occur in conjugate pairs.

(iii) POLES OF H(s)

The poles of $H(s)$ lie on the root-loci and correspond to $\xi = 0$.

This is proved by noting that when $\xi = 0$ the characteristic equation (6.1) becomes $P(s) = 0$, whose roots are the poles of $H(s)$ $(= Q(s)/P(s))$.

(iv) ZEROS OF H(s)

The zeros of $H(s)$ lie on the root-loci and correspond to $\xi = \pm\infty$.

This becomes apparent if equation (6.2) is written in the form

$$\frac{1}{\xi} + H(s) = 0.$$

It is then evident that as $\xi \to \pm\infty$, $H(s) \to 0$.

(v) ASYMPTOTES OF ROOT-LOCI

If $H(s)$ has r more poles than zeros, the root-loci are asymptotic to r straight lines making angles $(2k + 1)\pi/r$ $(k = 0, 1, 2, \ldots, r - 1)$ with the real axis, and also to r straight lines making angles $2k\pi/r$ $(k = 0, 1, 2, \ldots, r - 1)$ with the real axis. The root-loci approach the former asymptotes when $\xi \to +\infty$ and the latter when $\xi \to -\infty$.

This rule can be obtained by noting that if

$$H(s) = \frac{s^m + a_1 s^{m-1} + \ldots + a_m}{s^n + b_1 s^{n-1} + \ldots + b_n}, \tag{6.7}$$

where $r = n - m > 0$, then it can be deduced from equation (6.2) that

$$\frac{1}{H(s)} = s^r + (b_1 - a_1)s^{r-1} + \ldots = -\xi.$$

This indicates that $|\xi| \to \infty$ when $|s| \to \infty$. Furthermore, since the first two terms dominate the expression for $1/H(s)$ when $|s| \to \infty$, the last equation is then approximately

$$(s - \sigma_0)^r = -\xi = \left. \begin{array}{ll} |\xi| \exp\{i(2k + 1)\pi\}, & (\xi > 0), \\ |\xi| \exp\{i(2k)\pi\}, & (\xi < 0), \end{array} \right\} \quad (6.8.)$$

where $\sigma_0 = -(b_1 - a_1)/r$ and k is any integer. Each of equations (6.8) has r distinct solutions given by

$$s - \sigma_0 = \left. \begin{array}{ll} |\xi|^{1/r} \exp\{i(2k + 1)\pi/r\}, & (\xi > 0), \\ |\xi|^{1/r} \exp\{i(2k)\pi/r\}, & (\xi < 0), \end{array} \right\}$$

where $k = 0, 1, 2, \ldots, r - 1$. Putting $s = \sigma + i\omega$ and equating real and imaginary parts yields

$$\left. \begin{array}{l} \sigma - \sigma_0 = |\xi|^{1/r} \cos(2k + 1)\pi/r, \\ \omega = |\xi|^{1/r} \sin(2k + 1)\pi/r, \end{array} \right\} \quad (\xi > 0)$$

and

$$\left. \begin{array}{l} \sigma - \sigma_0 = |\xi|^{1/r} \cos 2k\pi/r, \\ \omega = |\xi|^{1/r} \sin 2k\pi/r, \end{array} \right\} \quad (\xi < 0)$$

from which it may be deduced by division that

$$\omega = \left. \begin{array}{ll} (\sigma - \sigma_0) \tan(2k + 1)\pi/r, & (\xi > 0), \\ (\sigma - \sigma_0) \tan 2k\pi/r, & (\xi < 0). \end{array} \right\} \quad (6.9)$$

These are the equations of the asymptotes of the root-loci. Since $k = 0, 1, 2, \ldots, r - 1$, each of equations (6.9) represents a family of r straight lines in the s-plane. The angular inclinations of these lines with the real axis are given by $(2k + 1)\pi/r$ and $2k\pi/r$ when $\xi > 0$ and $\xi < 0$, respectively.

It is important to note that asymptotes of this type do not exist if $H(s)$ has the same number of poles and zeros; for if $m = n$ it is clear from (6.7) and (6.2) that $H(s) \to 1$ and $\xi \to -1$ as $|s| \to \infty$.

(vi) POINT OF INTERSECTION OF ASYMPTOTES

Both sets of asymptotes intersect on the real axis at a point with abscissa

$$\sigma_0 = \left(\sum_{j=1}^{n} p_j - \sum_{j=1}^{m} z_j \right) / r,$$

where the p_j and z_j are respectively the poles and zeros of $H(s)$.

It is clear from equations (6.9) that, in both cases, $\omega = 0$ when

$$\sigma = \sigma_0 = -(b_1 - a_1)/r$$

for all values of k. All the asymptotes therefore intersect on the real axis at the point $(\sigma_0, 0)$. The abscissa σ_0 has the value quoted above since it can be deduced from the expression for $H(s)$ given in equation (6.7) that $a_1 = -\sum\limits_{j=1}^{m} z_j$ and $b_1 = -\sum\limits_{j=1}^{n} p_j$.

(vii) ROOT-LOCI ON THE REAL AXIS

If $H(s)$ has at least one real pole or zero, the whole of the real axis is occupied by root-loci: a segment of the real axis corresponds to positive or negative values of ξ according as an odd or an even number of poles and zeros of $H(s)$ lie to its right.

The arguments of the complex numbers represented by the vectors drawn from the conjugate complex poles or zeros of $H(s)$ to any point on the real axis cancel out in pairs. The argument of a vector drawn from a real pole or zero lying to the left of a point on the real axis is zero, whilst the corresponding quantity for a real pole or zero lying to the right is $-\pi$. It follows that the first of equations (6.6b) will be satisfied on the real axis only at those points having an odd number of poles and zeros to their right, and that the second of equations (6.6b) will be satisfied only when this number is even. Note that, in this context, zero is regarded as an even number.

(viii) BREAK-AWAY POINTS

Break-away points indicate the existence of multiple characteristic roots and occur at those values of s which satisfy $d\xi/ds = 0$.

Consider a characteristic equation which has a root of multiplicity $q(\geqslant 2)$ at $s = s_0$ when $\xi = \xi_0$. In the root-locus diagram for such an equation, q loci will converge on the point $s = s_0$ as ξ increases towards the value ξ_0 and will then 'break-away' from this common point as ξ increases beyond ξ_0. Typical break-away points are shown in Fig. 6.1: in Figs. 6.1(a) and (b), A and B each represent two equal real roots; and in Fig. 6.1(c), C and D each represent two equal complex roots and E represents two equal real roots.

The rule for determining the location of the break-away points can be derived by writing the characteristic equation (6.1) in the form

$$f(s, \xi) = P(s) + \xi Q(s) = 0.$$

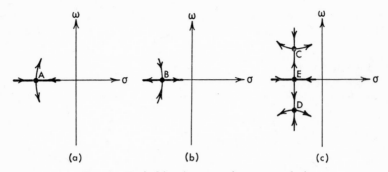

(a)   (b)   (c)

FIG. 6.1. Typical break-away points on root-loci.

It then follows that

$$\frac{df}{ds} = \frac{\partial f}{\partial s} + \frac{\partial f}{\partial \xi}\frac{d\xi}{ds} = 0$$

and consequently that

$$\frac{d\xi}{ds} = -\frac{\partial f/\partial s}{Q(s)} \tag{6.10}$$

since clearly $\partial f/\partial \xi = Q(s)$. Also, since

$$f(s, \xi_0) = (s - s_0)^q g(s),$$

where $g(s)$ is some function such that $g(s_0) \neq 0$, it is evident that

$$\frac{\partial f(s, \xi_0)}{\partial s} = q(s - s_0)^{q-1} g(s) + (s - s_0)^q g'(s).$$

This result and equation (6.10) together imply that

$$\left(\frac{d\xi}{ds}\right)_{s=s_0} = 0$$

if $Q(s_0) \neq 0$.

(ix) INTERSECTIONS OF ROOT-LOCI WITH THE IMAGINARY AXIS

The intersections of root-loci with the imaginary axis can be determined by calculating the values of ξ which result in the existence of imaginary characteristic roots.

These values of ξ, together with the corresponding imaginary roots, can be found from Routh's array as explained in Chapter 4, or by means of Orlando's theorem as explained in Chapter 5.

(x) SLOPES OF ROOT-LOCI AT COMPLEX POLES AND ZEROS OF H(s)

The slope of a root-locus at a complex pole or zero of H(s) can be found by applied equations (6.6b) to a point in the neighbourhood of the pole or zero.

This technique can be illustrated by considering the complex pole P_1 shown in Fig. 6.2, where x is the unknown slope of the locus at P_1.

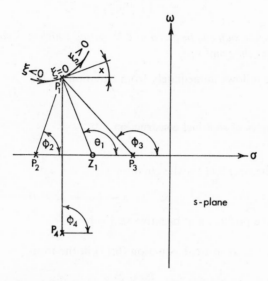

Fig. 6.2. Determination of slope of a root-locus at a complex pole.

The arguments of the complex numbers represented by the vectors drawn from the other poles P_2, P_3, P_4 and the zero Z_1 to a point on the root-locus near P_1 obviously differ very little from the angles ϕ_2, ϕ_3, ϕ_4, θ_1. If the first of equations (6.6b) is applied to a point in the neighbourhood of P_1 for which $\zeta > 0$, it therefore follows that

$$\theta_1 - \phi_2 - \phi_3 - \phi_4 - x = (2k + 1)\pi,$$

where k is an appropriate integer. The last equation can be solved for x since the angles ϕ_2, ϕ_3, ϕ_4 and θ_1 can easily be measured. Note that, alternatively, the slope of the root-locus could be found by applying the second of equations (6.6b) to a point in the neighbourhood of P_1 for which $\zeta < 0$.

(xi) CALCULATION OF ξ ON THE ROOT-LOCI

The absolute magnitude of the value of ξ corresponding to any point s_0
on a root-locus can be found by measuring the lengths of the vectors drawn
to s_0 from the poles and zeros of $H(s)$ and then evaluating

$$|\xi| = \frac{\prod\limits_{j=1}^{n} |s_0 - p_j|}{\prod\limits_{j=1}^{m} |s_0 - z_j|}.$$

The appropriate sign can be given to ξ by noting which of equations (6.6b)
is satisfied at the point s_0.

This rule follows immediately from equations (6.6).

6.4   Examples of root-loci construction

Example 1

Sketch the root-loci for the equation

$$s^4 + 5s^3 + 8s^2 + (6 + \xi)s + 2\xi = 0 \qquad (6.11)$$

if ξ can have positive and negative real values.

The first step is to write equation (6.11) in the form

$$1 + \xi\frac{(s + 2)}{s(s + 3)(s^2 + 2s + 2)} = 0$$

which indicates that, in the notation of equations (6.2) and (6.3),

$$H(s) = \frac{(s + 2)}{s(s + 3)(s^2 + 2s + 2)}.$$

This function has poles at $s = 0$, -3, $-1 + i$, $-1 - i$, and a zero at
$s = -2$. The root-loci for equation (6.11) can be sketched by using the
rules given in the last section as follows:

(i) There are four root-loci since equation (6.11) is of the fourth
degree.
(ii) The loci are symmetrical about the real axis since equation (6.11)
has real coefficients.
(iii) The loci pass through the poles at $s = 0$, -3, $-1 \pm i$ when
$\xi = 0$.

(iv) The loci pass through the zero at $s = -2$ when $\xi = \pm\infty$.

(v) $H(s)$ has three more poles than zeros, i.e., $r = 3$. It follows that three root-loci approach asymptotes with angular slopes given by

$$\frac{(2k + 1)\pi}{3} \quad (k = 0, 1, 2)$$

as $\xi \to +\infty$, and three loci approach asymptotes with slopes given by

$$\frac{2k\pi}{3} \quad (k = 0, 1, 2)$$

as $\xi \to -\infty$.

(vi) Both sets of asymptotes intersect on the real axis at the point with abscissa

$$\sigma_0 = \frac{\sum\limits_{j=1}^{n} p_j - \sum\limits_{j=1}^{m} z_j}{r} = \frac{(0 - 3 - 1 + i - 1 - i) - (-2)}{3} = -1.$$

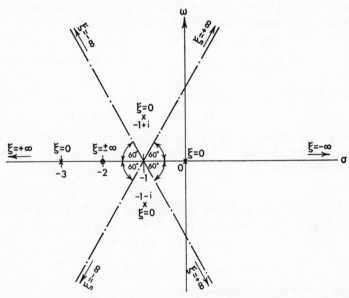

Fig. 6.3. Properties of root-loci for equation 6.11 obtained from rules (i)–(vi).

The properties of the loci obtained so far are summarised in Fig. 6.3 where zeros and poles of $H(s)$ are denoted by circles and crosses, respectively.

(vii) The whole of the real axis is occupied by root-loci. The negative real axis between the origin and $s = -2$ and to the left of $s = -3$

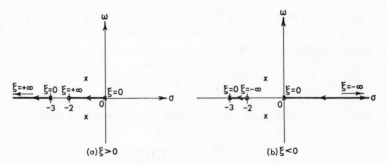

Fig. 6.4. Segments of root-loci for equation 6.11 lying on the real axis.

corresponds to $\xi > 0$, as shown in Fig. 6.4(a): the rest of the real axis corresponds to $\xi < 0$, as shown in Fig. 6.4(b).

(viii) There are no break-away points.

(ix) The values of ξ for which the loci intersect the imaginary axis can be found by either Routh's array or Orlando's theorem. The latter method involves the evaluation of the penultimate Hurwitz determinant which in the case of equation (6.11) is

$$\Delta_3 = \begin{vmatrix} 5 & 6+\xi & 0 \\ 1 & 8 & 2\xi \\ 0 & 5 & 6+\xi \end{vmatrix} = -\xi^2 - 22\xi + 204.$$

This determinant vanishes when

$$\xi = 5\sqrt{13} - 11 \quad \text{and} \quad \xi = -5\sqrt{13} - 11.$$

However, all the coefficients in equation (6.11) are positive only when ξ has the former value. It therefore follows from Orlando's theorem that eqution (6.11) has imaginary roots only when

$$\xi = 5\sqrt{13} - 11.$$

These roots can be found by putting $s = i\omega$ in (6.11) and then equating real and imaginary parts to zero. This gives

$$\left. \begin{array}{r} -5\omega^3 + (6 + \xi)\omega = 0, \\ \omega^4 - 8\omega^2 + 2\xi = 0. \end{array} \right\}$$

The first of these equations yields

$$\omega^2 = \sqrt{13} - 1 \quad \text{when} \quad \xi = 5\sqrt{13} - 11,$$

so that the required imaginary roots are $s = \pm i(\sqrt{13} - 1)^{\frac{1}{2}}$. It can be verified that the second equation is satisfied by $\omega^2 = \sqrt{13} - 1$, $\xi = 5\sqrt{13} - 11$.

(x) The slope of the tangent to the root-locus at the pole $s = -1 + i$ can be found by applying equation (6.6b) to a point in the vicinity of the pole, as shown in Fig. 6.5. If x is the angle of departure of the locus from the pole, since ξ is assumed to be positive it follows that

$$45° - 30° - 90° - 135° - x = (2k + 1)180°$$

which gives $x = -30°$. By symmetry, the angle of departure from the conjugate pole at $-1 - i$ is $+30°$.

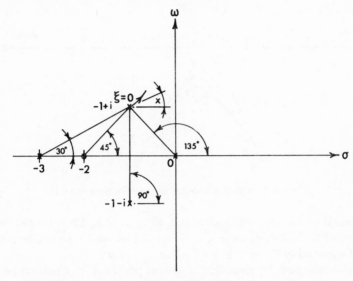

Fig. 6.5. Slopes of root-loci for equation 6.11 at the complex poles.

(xi) Rule (xi) can be used to calculate the value of ξ corresponding to any desired point on the complete root-locus diagram sketched in Fig. 6.6.

The behaviour of the four roots of equation (6.11) as ξ increases from $-\infty$ to $+\infty$ can now be readily described with the aid of Fig. 6.6. Thus, when $\xi = -\infty$ there is one real root (s_1) equal to -2, two complex roots (s_2, s_3) of infinite modulus, and one real root (s_4) at $s = +\infty$. If the value of ξ is increased, the real root s_1 moves along the negative real axis away from $s = -2$ and reaches the pole at $s = -3$ when $\xi = 0$; the two complex roots s_2 and s_3 move into the finite part of the s-plane and approach the poles at $s = -1 \pm i$ as $\xi \to 0$; and the real root s_4 moves along the positive real axis and reaches the pole at the origin when $\xi = 0$. If the value of ξ is increased further, the value of s_1 approaches $-\infty$ as $\xi \to +\infty$; the common real part of the conjugate complex roots s_2, s_3 becomes progressively less negative until the roots

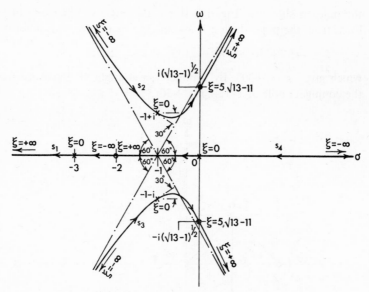

Fig. 6.6. Complete root-locus diagram for equation 6.11.

eventually cross the imaginary axis when $\xi = 5\sqrt{13} - 11$ and then move off to infinity again as $\xi \to +\infty$; and the root s_4 leaves the origin and approaches the zero at $s = -2$ as $\xi \to +\infty$.

It should now be clear that a system governed by equation (4.12) will be asymptotically stable only if $0 < \xi < 5\sqrt{13} - 11$. The root-locus diagram given in Fig. 6.6 can also be used to find the values of ξ sufficient to ensure a specified margin of absolute or relative stability: it is only necessary to superimpose the boundaries of the appropriate domains of the s-plane (of the types shown in Figs. 5.1 and 5.3) on the root-locus diagram, and then use rule (xi) to calculate the values of ξ at the points of intersection of these boundaries and the root-loci.

Example 2

Sketch the root-loci for the equation

$$s^4 + 2s^3 + 2s^2 + s + \xi = 0 \qquad (6.12)$$

if ξ is restricted to have positive real values.

Equation (6.12) may be written in the form

$$1 + \xi \frac{1}{s(s + 1)(s^2 + s + 1)} = 0$$

which indicates that, in the notation of equations (6.2) and (6.3),

$$H(s) = \frac{1}{s(s + 1)(s^2 + s + 1)}.$$

It is evident that $H(s)$ has poles at $s = 0, -1, -\frac{1}{2} + i\frac{1}{2}\sqrt{3}, -\frac{1}{2} - i\frac{1}{2}\sqrt{3}$, and no finite zeros. The root-loci for equation (6.12) can be sketched by using the rules given in the last section, remembering that in the present example $\xi > 0$:

(i) There are four root-loci since equation (6.12) is of the fourth degree.

(ii) The loci are symmetrical about the real axis since equation (6.12) has real coefficients.

(iii) The loci start from the poles at $s = 0, -1, -\frac{1}{2} + i\frac{1}{2}\sqrt{3}, -\frac{1}{2} - i\frac{1}{2}\sqrt{3}$ when $\xi = 0$.

(iv) This rule does not apply since $H(s)$ has no finite zeros.

(v) $H(s)$ has four more poles than zeros, i.e., $r = 4$. It follows that the four root-loci approach asymptotes with angular slopes given by

$$\frac{(2k + 1)\pi}{4} \quad (k = 0, 1, 2, 3)$$

as $\xi \to +\infty$. These are the only asymptotes that need be considered since it is stipulated that $\xi > 0$.

(vi) The asymptotes intersect on the real axis at the point with abscissa

$$\sigma_0 = \left(\sum_{j=1}^{n} p_j - \sum_{j=1}^{m} z_j \right) / r$$

$$= \frac{(0 - 1 - \frac{1}{2} + i\frac{1}{2}\sqrt{3} - \frac{1}{2} - i\frac{1}{2}\sqrt{3}) - (0)}{4} = -\frac{1}{2}.$$

The properties of the loci obtained so far are summarised in Fig. 6.7 where, as usual, poles of $H(s)$ are denoted by crosses.

(vii) Since $\xi > 0$, only that part of the real axis lying between the origin and $s = -1$ is occupied by root-loci, as shown in Fig. 6.8.

(viii) Equation (6.12) implies that

$$\xi = -(s^4 + 2s^3 + 2s^2 + s)$$

so that

$$\frac{d\xi}{ds} = -(4s^3 + 6s^2 + 4s + 1) = -(2s + 1)(2s^2 + 2s + 1).$$

This derivative is zero when $s = -\frac{1}{2}, -\frac{1}{2} + i\frac{1}{2}$, or $-\frac{1}{2} - i\frac{1}{2}$, which are therefore the break-away points on the root-loci.

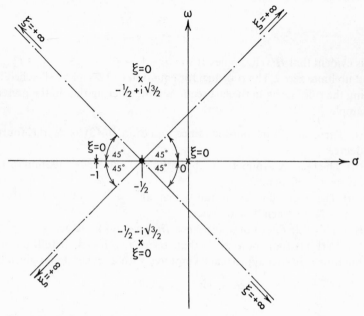

Fig. 6.7. Properties of root-loci for equation 6.12 obtained from rules (i)–(vi).

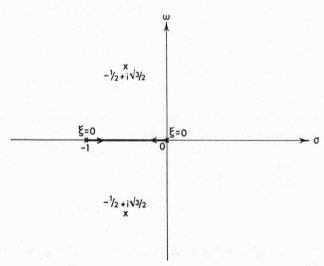

Fig. 6.8. Segment of root-loci for equation 6.12 lying on the real axis.

(ix) The penultimate Hurwitz determinant for equation (6.12) is

$$\Delta_3 = \begin{vmatrix} 2 & 1 & 0 \\ 1 & 2 & \xi \\ 0 & 2 & 1 \end{vmatrix} = 3 - 4\xi$$

which clearly vanishes when $\xi = \frac{3}{4}$. Since all the coefficients in equation (6.12) are then positive, it follows from Orlando's theorem that (6.12) has imaginary roots when $\xi = \frac{3}{4}$. Putting $s = i\omega$ in equation (6.12) to find these roots yields

$$\left. \begin{array}{r} -2\omega^3 + \omega = 0, \\ \omega^4 - 2\omega^2 + \xi = 0, \end{array} \right\}$$

on equating real and imaginary parts to zero. The first of these equations gives $\omega^2 = \frac{1}{2}$, indicating that the required imaginary roots are $s = \pm i/\sqrt{2}$. It can easily be verified that the second equation is satisfied by $\omega^2 = \frac{1}{2}$, $\xi = \frac{3}{4}$.

(x) The slope of the tangent to the root-locus at the pole

$$s = -\tfrac{1}{2} + i\tfrac{1}{2}\sqrt{3}$$

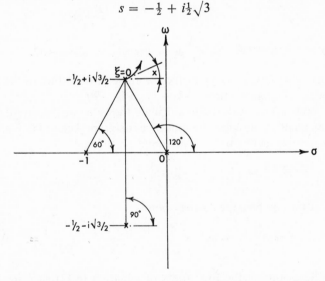

Fig. 6.9. Slopes of root-loci for equation 6.12 at the complex poles.

can be found by applying equation (6.6b) to a point in the vicinity of the pole, as shown in Fig. 6.9. Since $\xi > 0$, it follows from the diagram that the required angle, x, is given by

$$-60° - 90° - 120° - x = (2k + 1)180°$$

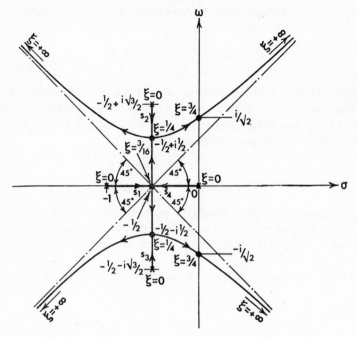

Fig. 6.10. Complete root-locus diagram for equation 6.12.

so that $x = -90°$. By symmetry the angle of departure of the locus from the conjugate pole at $-\frac{1}{2} - i\frac{1}{2}\sqrt{3}$ is $+90°$.

(xi) Rule (xi) can be used to calculate the value of ξ corresponding to any point on the complete root-locus diagram sketched in Fig. 6.10. For example, at the break-away point on the real axis

$$\xi = \prod_{j=1}^{n} |s_0 - p_j| = \frac{1}{2} \cdot \frac{1}{2} \cdot \frac{\sqrt{3}}{2} \cdot \frac{\sqrt{3}}{2} = \frac{3}{16},$$

and at the complex break-away points

$$\xi = \prod_{j=1}^{n} |s_0 - p_j| = \frac{1}{\sqrt{2}} \cdot \frac{1}{\sqrt{2}} \cdot \frac{\sqrt{3}-1}{2} \cdot \frac{\sqrt{3}+1}{2} = \frac{1}{4}.$$

The behaviour of the four roots of equation (6.12) as ξ increases from 0 to $+\infty$ can now be described. Thus, when $\xi = 0$ it is evident from Fig. 6.10 that there is one real root (s_1) equal to -1, two conjugate complex roots (s_2, s_3) at $s = -\frac{1}{2} \pm i\frac{1}{2}\sqrt{3}$, and one real root (s_4) at the origin. If the value of ξ is increased from zero, the roots s_1 and s_4 approach each other along the real axis, and the complex roots s_2 and s_3 move towards the complex break-away points at $s = -\frac{1}{2} \pm i\frac{1}{2}$.

When $\xi = \frac{3}{16}$, the roots s_1 and s_4 coincide at $s = -\frac{1}{2}$ and then break-away from the real-axis if ξ is increased further (for the sake of definiteness, s_1 will be regarded as moving upwards and s_4 downwards†). Eventually, when $\xi = \frac{1}{4}$, s_1 and s_2 coincide at $s = -\frac{1}{2} + i\frac{1}{2}$, and s_3 and s_4 coincide at $s = -\frac{1}{2} - i\frac{1}{2}$. If ξ is then increased beyond $\xi = \frac{1}{4}$, s_1 and s_2 break-away from $s = -\frac{1}{2} + i\frac{1}{2}$ and become distinct complex roots, and s_3 and s_4 break-away from $s = -\frac{1}{2} - i\frac{1}{2}$ in a similar fashion. If s_2 and s_3 are regarded as moving to the right after break-away, they eventually cross the imaginary axis when $\xi = \frac{3}{4}$, and have positive real parts if $\xi > \frac{3}{4}$. It may therefore be concluded that the system governed by equation (6.12) will be asymptotically stable only if $0 < \xi < \frac{3}{4}$. It is interesting to note from Fig. 6.10 that all four roots s_1, s_2, s_3, s_4 have real parts equal to $-\frac{1}{2}$ when $\frac{3}{16} < \xi < \frac{1}{4}$. If the value of ξ lies in this interval it follows that all components of transient response will be damped sinusoids whose amplitudes decay as $e^{-t/2}$.

Problems

1. Plot loci showing the variation of the roots of the following characteristic equations as the value of the real parameter ξ increases from $-\infty$ to $+\infty$:

   (a) $s^2 + (5 + \xi)s + \xi = 0$.
   (b) $s^3 + (2 + \xi)s^2 + (4 - 2\xi)s + \xi = 0$.
   (c) $s^3 + (5 + \xi)s^2 + (6 + \xi)s + 2\xi = 0$.
   (d) $s^4 + \xi s^3 + (7\xi - 5)s^2 + 12\xi s + 4 = 0$.

2. The characteristic equation of a system has the form

   $$s^3 + 6s^2 + 8s + \xi = 0,$$

   where ξ is a positive real parameter. Plot the root-loci for this equation and hence determine the value of ξ which will cause the system to be asymptotically stable and to have an oscillatory impulse response component with a dimensionless damping parameter $v = 0.5$.

3. Plot the root-loci for a second-order system having the characteristic equation

   $$ms^2 + cs + k = 0$$

   in the following cases:

   (a) m variable, $c = k = 1$.
   (b) c variable, $m = k = 1$.
   (c) k variable, $m = c = 1$.

† It should be noted that this is an assumption made for descriptive convenience: for it is not possible, using root-locus techniques alone, to identify the path taken by an individual root as it passes through a break-away point.

4. Plot the characteristic root-loci for unity-feedback closed-loop control systems having the following open-loop transfer functions, where $\xi(> 0)$ is the open-loop gain in each case:

(a) $\dfrac{\xi}{s(s + 2)}$.

(b) $\dfrac{\xi}{s^2 + 4s + 3}$.

(c) $\dfrac{\xi}{s^2 + s + 1}$.

(d) $\dfrac{\xi}{s(s + 1)(s + 4)}$.

(e) $\dfrac{\xi(s^2 + 2s + 2)}{(s + 3)(s^2 + s + 3)}$.

5. The quartic equation

$$s^4 + as^3 + bs^2 + cs + d = 0$$

can be written in the form

$$\{[(s + a)s + b]s + c\}s + d = 0.$$

Use this fact to show that the roots of the quartic can be found by plotting a sequence of root-loci for the equations

$$1 + \xi_r G_r(s) = 0 \quad (r = 1, 2, 3),$$

where

$$G_1(s) = \frac{1}{(s + a)s},$$

$$G_2(s) = \frac{1}{[(s + a)s + b]s},$$

$$G_3(s) = \frac{1}{\{[(s + a)s + b]s + c\}s},$$

and the ξ_r are assigned appropriate values. Generalise this technique so as to provide a means of determining the roots of an algebraic equation of arbitrary degree.†

6. An aircraft which is unstable in longitudinal motion in the absence

† W. R. Evans, *Control system dynamics*, p. 129, McGraw-Hill, 1954.

of an autopilot may be characterised as a unity-feedback closed-loop control system having an open-loop transfer function†

$$G(s) = \frac{\xi}{s} \frac{(s + 0\cdot 8)}{(s + 2\cdot 52)(s - 0\cdot 92)} \left(\frac{s + 1}{s + 6}\right) \frac{1}{(s + 6\cdot 5)^2 + 121}$$

when an autopilot is employed. Plot the root-loci for the characteristic equation of the closed-loop system, and hence determine whether it is possible to choose ξ(> 0) so as to stabilise the aircraft.

† W. Bollay, Aerodynamic stability and automatic control, *J. Aero. Sci.*, 13, 569, 1951; J-C. Grille, *et al.*, op. cit., p. 250.

Chapter 7

METHOD OF D-PARTITION

7.1 D-partition boundaries

If the coefficients in the characteristic equation

$$F(s) = a_0 s^n + a_1 s^{n-1} + \ldots + a_{n-1}s + a_n = 0 \qquad (7.1)$$

are functions of m system parameters $\xi, \eta, \ldots$, then root-loci can show the effect of varying only one of the parameters at a time. However, it is possible to avoid this restriction to only one system parameter (and at the same time retain a direct graphical representation of stability characteristics) by classifying instances of equation (7.1) according to the nature of their roots instead of plotting the roots themselves, as in the root-locus method.

This classification can be achieved by regarding each set of values of the m system parameters $\xi, \eta, \ldots$, as the coordinates of a point in an m-dimensional space, thus setting-up a correspondence between points of this space and instances of equation (7.1): each point of the system parameter space can then be classified according to the number of roots of the corresponding characteristic equation that have negative real parts. In this way the parameter space can be divided into domains $D(k, n - k)$ $(0 \leqslant k \leqslant n)$, where $D(k, n - k)$ contains all those points representing instances of equation (7.1) having k roots with negative real parts and $n - k$ roots with positive real parts; in particular, it is possible to determine the *domain of asymptotic stability* $D(n, 0)$ which contains all those points representing asymptotically stable instances of equation (7.1). This process is known as the *D-partition* of the system parameter space.†

The necessary procedure for determining the boundaries of the domains $D(k, n - k)$ $(0 \leqslant k \leqslant n)$ can be inferred from the discussion of stability boundaries given in Section 5.4. It will be recalled that, apart from the possibility of a characteristic root jumping from $-\infty$ to $+\infty$, an increase in the number of roots having positive real parts can occur

† Y. I. Neimark, On the problem of the distribution of the roots of polynomials, *Dokl. Akcd. Nauk. SSSR*, **58**, 357, 1947; Structure of the D-partition of the space of polynomials and the diagrams of Vishnegradskii and Nyquist, *Dokl. Akad. Nauk. SSSR*, **59**, 853, 1948.

only as a result of a root crossing the imaginary axis from the left to the right half of the s-plane. A root crossing the imaginary axis in this way corresponds to the representative point $(\xi, \eta, \ldots)$ moving from a domain $D(k, n - k)$ to the domain $D(k - 1, n - k + 1)$ of the system parameter space. The D-partition boundaries for finite characteristic roots are therefore simply the map of the imaginary axis

$$s = i\omega \, (-\infty < \omega < +\infty)$$

in the parameter space. In addition, it is necessary to include the D-partition boundaries corresponding to infinite roots: these are given by the surface $a_0(\xi, \eta, \ldots) = 0$, since equations of the form (7.1) have infinite roots when $a_0 = 0$.

It is, of course, impossible actually to construct the D-partition boundaries in system parameter spaces having more than three dimensions. Furthermore, since in three-dimensional parameter space the D-partition boundaries are two-dimensional surfaces, the usefulness of the method of D-partition is in practice confined to the investigation of the dependence of system stability on the values of one or two parameters. However, in such cases the method of D-partition is often a more efficient and informative means of constructing domains of stability than any method based upon the graphical interpretation of algebraic criteria such as those of Routh and Hurwitz.

7.2 Domains of stability in one-dimensional parameter space

In cases where the coefficients in the characteristic equation depend linearly on only one parameter, ξ, equation (7.1) can be written in the form

$$F(s) = P(s) + \xi Q(s) = 0. \tag{7.2}$$

This can be solved to give

$$\xi = -\frac{P(s)}{Q(s)}$$

which implies that the values of ξ corresponding to the imaginary axis in the s-plane are given by

$$\xi(\omega) = -\frac{P(i\omega)}{Q(i\omega)} (-\infty < \omega < +\infty). \tag{7.3}$$

Equation (7.3) therefore defines the D-partition boundaries corresponding to finite roots. If these boundaries are shaded on the left-hand side as ω increases from $-\infty$ to $+\infty$, then the shaded side of a D-partition boundary will correspond to the left-hand (i.e., stable) side of the imaginary axis in the s-plane. Thus, crossing a D-partition boundary from the shaded to the unshaded side will correspond to a characteristic root passing from the left to the right half of the s-plane. Note that in cases where the coefficient of s^n in equation (7.1) is a function of the parameter ξ, the characteristic equation will have an infinite root at the *singular point* $a_0(\xi) = 0$.

If the complete set of D-partition boundaries is shaded in accordance with the foregoing convention, it is possible to determine the value of k appropriate to each of the domains $D(k, n - k)$ if the value of k for any one domain is known. This can be done simply by observing the number of times a D-partition boundary is crossed, and decreasing or increasing the value of k according as the crossing is from the shaded to the unshaded side or vice versa. In this way the domain of asymptotic stability $D(n, 0)$ can be identified. It should be noted that if ξ is restricted to real values, the domain of asymptotic stability reduces to those segments of the real axis which lie within $D(n, 0)$.

As an illustration of this technique of constructing domains of asymptotic stability for equations of the form (7.2), consider the characteristic equation

$$F(s) = s^3 + 5s^2 + 6s + \xi = 0. \tag{7.4}$$

In this case,

$$\xi = -s^3 - 5s^2 - 6s$$

which gives

$$\xi(\omega) = 5\omega^2 + i(\omega^3 - 6\omega) \tag{7.5}$$

on putting $s = i\omega$.

Since the coefficient of s^3 in equation (7.4) is independent of ξ, there is no singular point and so the complete set of D-partition boundaries is obtained by letting ω increase from $-\infty$ to $+\infty$ in equation (7.5). The resulting locus is shown in Fig. 7.1 where it will be noted that the shading always lies to the left as ω increases. The various domains into which the ξ-plane is divided can be identified by observing that when $\xi = 2$, one root of equation (7.4) is $s_1 = -1$. The two remaining roots are easily found by factorisation to be $s_2 = -2 + \sqrt{2}$ and $s_3 = -2 - \sqrt{2}$. Since all three roots are negative, it follows that the point $\xi = 2$ lies in the domain of asymptotic stability $D(3, 0)$. The other domains must therefore be $D(2, 1)$ and $D(1, 2)$, as shown. In this example, the domain $D(0, 3)$ does not exist. This indicates that equation (7.4) can never have three roots with positive real parts.

If ξ is a real parameter, the only relevant part of the domain of

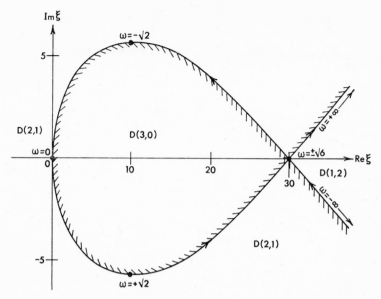

Fig. 7.1. D-partition diagram for equation 7.4.

asymptotic stability is the segment of the real axis lying within $D(3, 0)$. Thus, if ξ is real, Fig. 7.1 indicates that equation (7.4) represents an asymptotically stable system if and only if $0 < \xi < 30$. It may also be inferred from Fig. 7.1 that equation (7.4) has conjugate imaginary roots equal to $\pm i\sqrt{6}$ when $\xi = 30$. This agrees with the result obtained by Orlando's theorem in Section 5.4.

Since there is only one parameter in equation (7.4), all the information conveyed by Fig. 7.1 can be given equally well by root-loci if ξ is real. Thus, the root-loci for equation (7.4) plotted in Fig. 7.2 confirm that all the characteristic roots lie in the left half of the s-plane if and only if $0 < \xi < 30$, and that conjugate imaginary roots equal to $\pm i\sqrt{6}$ exist when $\xi = 30$.

In the last example, the coefficient of the highest power of s in the characteristic equation is independent of ξ. If this is not the case, the D-partition boundaries will include a singular point $a_0(\xi) = 0$ at which the characteristic equation has an infinite root. Consider, for example, the equation

$$F(s) = (1 + \xi)s^3 + s^2 + s + 6 = 0. \tag{7.6}$$

Solving for ξ gives

$$\xi = -1 - \frac{1}{s} - \frac{1}{s^2} - \frac{6}{s^3}.$$

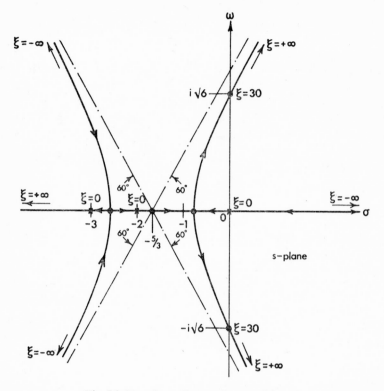

Fig. 7.2. Root-locus diagram for equation 7.4.

from which it follows that

$$\xi(\omega) = \left(-1 + \frac{1}{\omega^2}\right) + i\left(\frac{1}{\omega} - \frac{6}{\omega^3}\right). \qquad (7.7)$$

The curved lines shown in Fig. 7.3 are the D-partition boundaries obtained by letting ω increase from $-\infty$ to $+\infty$ in equation (7.7): as usual, the shading always lies to the left as ω increases. In this case there is a singular point at $\xi = -1$, since it is evident from equation (7.6) that the coefficient of s^3 vanishes when $\xi = -1$.

Now, when $\xi = 0$, equation (7.6) becomes

$$s^3 + s^2 + s + 6 = (s + 2)(s^2 - s + 3) = 0$$

which clearly has two roots with positive real parts. The origin in Fig. 7.3 therefore lies in $D(1, 2)$, and the domains $D(2, 1)$ and $D(3, 0)$ may consequently be identified as shown.

If ξ is real, it is evident from Fig. 7.3 that equation (7.6) represents

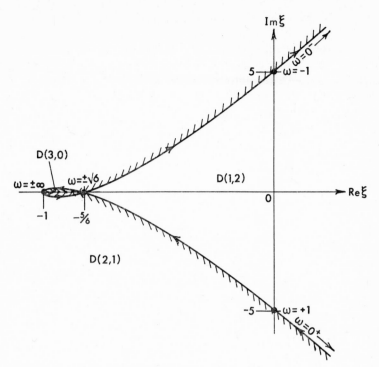

Fig. 7.3. *D*-partition diagram for equation 7.6.

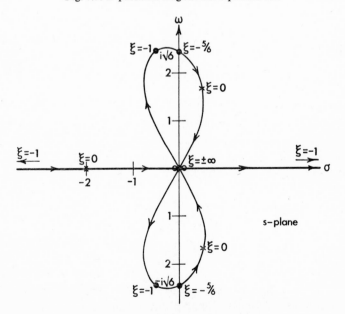

Fig. 7.4. Root-locus diagram for equation 7.6.

an asymptotically stable system if and only if $-1 < \xi < -\frac{5}{6}$. It can also be inferred that conjugate imaginary roots equal to $\pm i\sqrt{6}$ exist when $\xi = -\frac{5}{6}$. All this information is also given by the root-loci for equation (7.6) which are shown in Fig. 7.4. In addition, of course, the root-loci show the actual values of the characteristic roots and not merely the numbers of roots having positive or negative real parts.

7.3 Domains of stability in two-dimensional parameter space

In cases where the coefficients in the characteristic equation depend linearly on two parameters, ξ and η, equation (7.1) can be written in the form

$$F(s) = \xi P(s) + \eta Q(s) + R(s) = 0. \tag{7.8}$$

If

$$P(i\omega) = P_1(\omega) + iP_2(\omega),$$

$$Q(i\omega) = Q_1(\omega) + iQ_2(\omega),$$

and

$$R(i\omega) = R_1(\omega) + iR_2(\omega),$$

putting $s = i\omega$ in equation (7.8) then yields

$$F(i\omega) = \xi P_1(\omega) + \eta Q_1(\omega) + R_1(\omega)$$
$$+ i\{\xi P_2(\omega) + \eta Q_2(\omega) + R_2(\omega)\} = 0$$

which implies that

$$\xi P_1(\omega) + \eta Q_1(\omega) + R_1(\omega) = 0,$$
$$\xi P_2(\omega) + \eta Q_2(\omega) + R_2(\omega) = 0. \tag{7.9}$$

These equations determine the D-partition boundaries corresponding to finite roots of equation (7.8).

Thus, if $\Delta(\omega) = P_1(\omega)Q_2(\omega) - P_2(\omega)Q_1(\omega) \neq 0$, equations (7.9) are non-singular and may be solved for ξ and η to give

$$\xi(\omega) = \frac{-R_1(\omega)Q_2(\omega) + R_2(\omega)Q_1(\omega)}{\Delta(\omega)},$$

$$\eta(\omega) = \frac{-R_2(\omega)P_1(\omega) + R_1(\omega)P_2(\omega)}{\Delta(\omega)}. \tag{7.10}$$

These equations define a locus which, as ω increases from $-\infty$ to $+\infty$, traces out in the ξ, η-plane a map of the imaginary axis in the s-plane: this map is accordingly part of the system of D-partition boundaries for equation (7.8). If $\Delta(\omega) = 0$ for some value of ω, the corresponding singular locus (actually a straight line) is also a D-partition boundary and can be found by substituting the appropriate value of ω into equations (7.9). In addition, if the coefficient of s^n in the characteristic equation is a function of ξ or η, the straight line a_0 (ξ, η) = 0 must be included as the D-partition boundary associated with infinite roots. Straight lines of both the last types are known as *singular lines*.

The various domains $D(k, n - k)$ ($0 \leqslant k \leqslant n$) into which the ξ, η-plane is divided by the D-partition boundaries can be identified by shading the boundaries in such a way that the shaded side always corresponds to the stable side of the imaginary axis in the s-plane. The nature of the appropriate shading can be inferred by taking one-dimensional cross-sections of the ξ, η-plane (by assigning fixed values to ξ or η in equation (7.8)) and then using the simple shading rule for one-parameter systems given in Section 7.2.† This technique can be used ab initio in each individual case or, alternatively, it can be used to derive a set of general rules‡ which are directly applicable to any system of D-partition boundaries in two-dimensional parameter space. In fact, it can be shown that if the axes in the ξ, η-plane constitute a right-handed orthogonal system, the non-singular locus defined by equations (7.10) must be shaded on the left when $\Delta > 0$ and on the right when $\Delta < 0$ if the locus is traversed in the direction of increasing ω. It is usually found that the same curve is traversed when ω increases from $-\infty$ to 0 as when ω increases from 0 to $+\infty$, and also that Δ changes sign when $\omega = 0$ or $\omega = \pm\infty$. In such circumstances the non-singular locus will be shaded twice on the same side (note that crossing a double-shaded boundary in the ξ, η-plane corresponds to two characteristic roots crossing the imaginary axis in the s-plane).

The rules‡ for shading a singular line depend upon the values of ω for which it intersects the non-singular locus. If the intersection occurs at a point on the non-singular locus at which Δ changes sign and $\omega = 0$, a singular line must be shaded as shown in Fig. 7.5(a). It will be noted that the singular and non-singular loci are shaded on the same side near the point of intersection but that beyond this point the shading passes to the other side of the singular line. The loci must be shaded similarly if they intersect at a point on the non-singular locus at which Δ changes sign and $\omega = \pm\infty$.

On the other hand, if the intersection occurs at a finite value of ω at which Δ changes sign, the loci must be shaded as shown in Fig. 7.5(b) if Δ also changes sign when $\omega = 0$.

† See Problem 2 at the end of this chapter, for example.
‡ See M. A. Aizerman, *Theory of automatic control*, Pergamon Press, 1963.

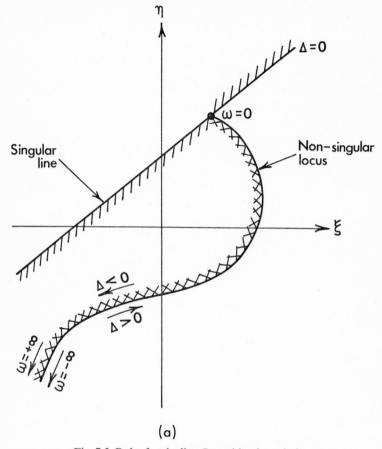

(a)

Fig. 7.5. Rules for shading D-partition boundaries.

Finally, in certain special circumstances Δ vanishes identically. If this happens the singular lines are the only D-partition boundaries.

As a first example of the construction of domains of asymptotic stability in two-dimensional parameter space, consider the characteristic equation

$$F(s) = s^3 + \xi s^2 + \xi s + \eta = 0, \qquad (7.11)$$

where ξ and η are real parameters. In this case,

$$F(i\omega) = -\omega^2 \xi + \eta + i(\omega \xi - \omega^3) = 0$$

and consequently

$$\left. \begin{array}{l} -\omega^2 \xi + \eta \quad\;\; = 0, \\[2mm] \omega \xi \quad\;\;\; -\omega^3 = 0. \end{array} \right\} \qquad (7.12)$$

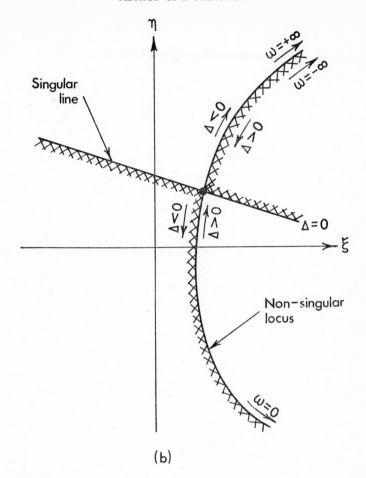

(b)

The determinant of equations (7.12) is $\Delta(\omega) = -\omega$, which is zero only when $\omega = 0$.

If $\omega \neq 0$ it may be deduced from equations (7.12) that

$$\xi = \omega^2, \qquad \eta = \omega^4.$$

It follows that the non-singular D-partition boundaries are given by the semi-parabola

$$\eta = \xi^2 \quad (\xi, \eta > 0) \tag{7.13}$$

shown in Fig. 7.6. This locus is shaded in accordance with the rules given above.

However, if $\omega = 0$, equations (7.12) imply that $\eta = 0$ and ξ is arbitrary: the ξ-axis is therefore a singular line which must be shaded as shown in Fig. 7.6 since the singular and non-singular loci intersect at a point where Δ changes sign and $\omega = 0$. This line completes the D-partition boundaries since the coefficient of s^3 in equation (7.11) is independent of ξ and η.

In Fig. 7.6, the point $\xi = 3$, $\eta = 1$ lies between the positive ξ-axis and the semi-parabola (7.13). Also, when $\xi = 3$ and $\eta = 1$ equation (7.11) becomes

$$s^3 + 3s^2 + 3s + 1 = (s + 1)^3 = 0$$

whose roots are all negative. It follows that the point $\xi = 3$, $\eta = 1$ lies in the domain of asymptotic stability $D(3, 0)$ and that, in view of the shading of the loci, the remaining regions of the ξ, η-plane are the domains $D(1, 2)$ and $D(2, 1)$, as indicated in Fig. 7.6. This chart can

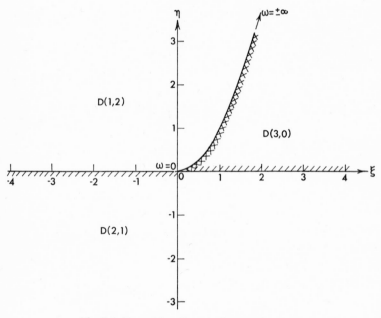

Fig. 7.6. D-partition diagram for equation 7.11.

be used to decide the stability of any system having a characteristic equation of the form (7.11).

As a second example of the construction of D-partition boundaries in two-dimensional parameter space, consider the characteristic equation

$$F(s) = s^3 + \xi s^2 + \eta s + 1 = 0, \tag{7.14}$$

where ξ and η are again real parameters. This equation was studied extensively by Vishnegradskii who pointed out that the more general cubic equation

$$a_0 z^3 + a_1 z^2 + a_2 z + a_3 = 0 \quad (a_0 > 0, \quad a_3 > 0)$$

can be reduced to the form (7.14) by choosing

$$s = (a_0/a_3)^{\frac{1}{3}}z, \qquad \xi = a_1/(a_0^2 a_3)^{\frac{1}{3}}, \qquad \eta = a_2/(a_0 a_3^2)^{\frac{1}{3}}. \qquad (7.15)$$

Substituting $s = i\omega$ in equation (7.14) gives

$$F(i\omega) = -\omega^2 \xi + 1 + i(\omega\eta - \omega^3) = 0$$

so that

$$\left.\begin{array}{r} -\omega^2\xi \quad + 1 = 0, \\ \omega\eta - \omega^2 = 0. \end{array}\right\} \qquad (7.16)$$

The determinant of equations (7.16) is $\Delta(\omega) = -\omega^3$ which vanishes only when $\omega = 0$.

If $\omega \neq 0$, it follows from equations (7.16) that

$$\xi = \frac{1}{\omega^2}, \qquad \eta = \omega,$$

and consequently that the non-singular D-partition boundary is given by

$$\xi\eta = 1 \quad (\xi, \eta > 0). \qquad (7.17)$$

The semi-hyperbola (7.17) is known as the *Vishnegradskii hyperbola* and is shown in Fig. 7.7. It is shaded in accordance with the rules given earlier in this section.

If $\omega = 0$, equations (7.16) imply that $\xi = \infty$ and η is arbitrary. In this case the singular locus therefore lies at infinity and so does not affect the D-partition of the ξ, η-plane. Thus, the only relevant D-partition boundary for equation (7.14) is the Vishnegradskii hyperbola (7.17).

When $\xi = 0$ and $\eta = 0$ the characteristic equation (7.14) becomes

$$s^3 + 1 = (s + 1)(s^2 - s + 1) = 0.$$

This equation has one negative real root and two conjugate complex roots with positive real parts. The origin of the ξ, η-plane in Fig. 7.7 therefore lies in the domain $D(1, 2)$. In view of the double shading, it follows that the region above and to the right of the Vishnegradskii hyperbola is the domain of asymptotic stability $D(3, 0)$. By using the transformations (7.15), the stability chart given in Fig. 7.7 can be used to analyse the stability of a wide class of systems having cubic characteristic equations.

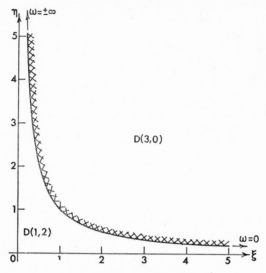

Fig. 7.7. D-partition diagram for equation 7.14
(Vishnegradskii hyperbola).

In both the previous examples the coefficient of the highest power of s in the characteristic equation is independent of the system parameters. If this is not the case, an additional singular line must be included as a D-partition boundary. This can be illustrated by constructing the domain of asymptotic stability for the characteristic equation

$$F(s) = \xi s^3 + (2\xi + 1)s^2 + (\xi + 1)s + 3\eta = 0. \qquad (7.18)$$

With $s = i\omega$ this becomes

$$F(i\omega) = -2\omega^2\xi + 3\eta - \omega^2 + i\{(-\omega^3 + \omega)\xi + \omega\} = 0$$

which implies that

$$\left.\begin{array}{c} -2\omega^2\xi + 3\eta - \omega^2 = 0, \\ (-\omega^3 + \omega)\xi + \omega = 0. \end{array}\right\} \qquad (7.19)$$

The determinant of equations (7.19) is $\Delta(\omega) = 3\omega(\omega^2 - 1)$ which vanishes when $\omega = 0$ or $\omega = \pm 1$.

It may be deduced from equations (7.19) that, except when $\Delta = 0$,

$$\xi = \frac{1}{\omega^2 - 1}, \qquad \eta = \frac{\omega^2(\omega^2 + 1)}{3(\omega^2 - 1)}. \qquad (7.20)$$

The non-singular locus defined by these equations as ω increases from $-\infty$ to $+\infty$ consists of two separate branches, as shown in Fig. 7.8.

In fact, this locus lies in the third quadrant of the ξ, η-plane when $0 < |\omega| < 1$, and in the first quadrant when $1 < |\omega| < \infty$. It will be noted that the whole of the non-singular locus has double shading, in accordance with the rules given at the beginning of this section.

Now the determinant of equations (7.19) vanishes when $\omega = 0$ or $\omega = \pm 1$. In the former case, it follows from equations (7.19) that $\eta = 0$ and ξ is arbitrary. Thus, the ξ-axis is the singular locus corresponding to $\omega = 0$ (it is clear by direct inspection that equation (7.18)

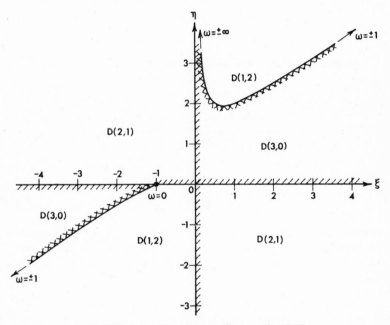

Fig. 7.8. D-partition diagram for equation 7.18.

has a root at the origin of the s-plane when $\eta = 0$): in Fig. 7.8 the ξ-axis is shaded in accordance with the convention illustrated in Fig. 7.5(a). In the second singular case when $\omega = \pm 1$, equations (7.19) imply that the values of ξ and η are infinite, as indicated in Fig. 7.8.

Since the coefficient of s^3 in equation (7.18) vanishes when $\xi = 0$, it is necessary to include the η-axis as an additional singular D-partition boundary. However, this boundary cannot be shaded until Fig. 7.8 and equation (7.18) have been examined in more detail. Thus, if $\xi = 1$ and $\eta = \frac{1}{3}$, equation (7.18) becomes

$$s^3 + 3s^2 + 2s + 1 = 0. \tag{7.21}$$

This is a cubic equation of the Vishnegradskii type (7.14), and so the stability chart given in Fig. 7.7 may be used. This indicates that all three roots of equation (7.21) have negative real parts and consequently that the point $\xi = 1$, $\eta = \frac{1}{3}$ lies in the domain of asymptotic stability, $D(3, 0)$, of Fig. 7.8. It follows that the η-axis must be shaded as shown.

The various domains into which the ξ, η-plane is divided may now be identified and are as indicated in Fig. 7.8. It will be noted that the domain of asymptotic stability lies in parts of both the first and third quadrants. Also, the domain $D(0, 3)$ does not exist.

7.4 Application to complex characteristic equations

The method of D-partition has so far been applied only to characteristic equations having real coefficients. However, the same basic approach can be used to construct the domains of asymptotic stability for systems governed by complex characteristic equations.

This can be illustrated by considering the whirling shaft whose stability was discussed in Section 4.7 and again in Section 5.5. It will be recalled that the characteristic equation of this system is

$$s^2 + 2v\omega_n s + (\omega_n^2 - 2iv\omega_n \Omega) = 0 \qquad (7.22)$$

where v is the damping parameter, ω_n the undamped natural frequency, and Ω the rotational speed. If a new variable $S = s/\Omega$ and new parameters $\xi = 2v\omega_n/\Omega$ and $\eta = (\omega_n/\Omega)^2$ are introduced, the last equation becomes

$$S^2 + \xi S + (\eta - i\xi) = 0. \qquad (7.23)$$

Substituting $S = i\omega$ in equation (7.23) gives

$$(\eta - \omega^2) + i(\omega - 1)\xi = 0$$

which indicates that

$$\left.\begin{array}{l} \eta - \omega^2 = 0, \\ (\omega - 1)\xi = 0. \end{array}\right\} \qquad (7.24)$$

These equations define the D-partition boundaries for equation (7.23): their determinant is clearly $\Delta(\omega) = 1 - \omega$.

If $\omega \neq 1$, equations (7.24) are non-singular and imply that

$$\xi = 0, \qquad \eta = \omega^2. \qquad (7.25)$$

When ω increases from $-\infty$ to $+\infty$, the locus defined by (7.25) describes the positive η-axis from infinity to the origin and then back to infinity again. However, since $\Delta > 0$ only when $-\infty < \omega < +1$, the η-axis must be shaded as shown in Fig. 7.9.

If $\omega = 1$, equations (7.24) imply that $\eta = 1$ and ξ is arbitrary. In order to complete the D-partition boundaries for equation (7.23) it is therefore necessary to include the singular line $\eta = 1$. The various domains of the ξ, η-plane may then be identified as indicated in Fig. 7.9, where the domain of asymptotic stability is $D(2, 0)$.

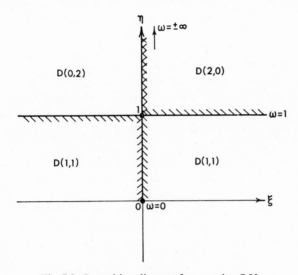

Fig. 7.9. *D*-partition diagram for equation 7.23.

Note that only the half-plane $\eta > 0$ is relevant since $\eta = (\omega_n/\Omega)^2$ and ω_n, Ω are real. Note also that both sides of the positive η-axis are shaded when $\eta < 1$. This indicates that although equation (7.23) has conjugate imaginary roots when $\xi = 0$ and $\eta < 1$, these roots cease to be conjugate when $\xi \neq 0$. Thus, crossing the η-axis in Fig. 7.9 when $\eta < 1$ corresponds to one complex root crossing the imaginary axis from the right to the left half of the S-plane and the other (non-conjugate) complex root crossing the imaginary axis in the opposite direction: as shown in Fig. 7.9, the total numbers of roots having positive and negative real parts therefore remain the same.

Since ξ is a non-negative quantity, it is evident from Fig. 7.9 that the system governed by equation (7.22) will be asymptotically stable only if $\eta = (\omega_n/\Omega)^2 > 1$, i.e., only if $\Omega < \omega_n$. This is the same result as was obtained more laboriously by Sturm's theorem and also by the generalised Hurwitz criterion.

7.5 Domains of absolute and relative stability

A domain of asymptotic stability in system parameter space corresponds to the whole of the left half of the s-plane. However, it is possible to use the method of D-partition to construct domains of parameter space corresponding to other regions of the s-plane—for example, to those regions shown in Figs. 5.1 and 5.3 which guarantee a specified margin of absolute or relative stability. This approach is often more convenient than that based on the Hurwitz inequalities given in Section 5.6.

If it is desired to use the method of D-partition to investigate the absolute stability of a linear system, it is necessary to introduce a new variable $S = s + \delta$ ($\delta > 0$) into the characteristic equation, as in Chapter 5. The resulting modified characteristic equation may then be used to map the imaginary axis of the S-plane on to the space of the system parameters. In this way, the space is divided into a number of domains $D(k, n - k; \delta)$ ($0 \leqslant k \leqslant n$). A typical domain $D(k, n - k; \delta)$ contains all those points representing combinations of parameter values which result in the modified characteristic equation having k roots in the left half of the S-plane (and which therefore result in the original characteristic equation having k roots with real parts less than $-\delta$). The domain $D(n, 0; \delta)$ is called the *domain of absolute stability* δ, since all systems whose parameters lie in this region have a transient response which decays at least as rapidly as $e^{-\delta t}$. $D(n, 0; \delta)$ ($\delta > 0$) lies within the domain of asymptotic stability $D(n, 0; 0) \equiv D(n, 0)$.

As an illustration of this method of investigating absolute stability consider again equation (7.11) whose domain of asymptotic stability was constructed in Fig. 7.6. With $S = s + \delta$, this equation becomes

$$F(S - \delta) \equiv G(S) = S^3 + (\xi - 3\delta)S^2 + (\xi - 2\delta\xi + 3\delta^2)S + (\delta^2\xi - \delta\xi + \eta - \delta^3) = 0. \quad (7.26)$$

Substituting $S = i\Omega$ now yields

$$G(i\Omega) = (-\Omega^2 - \delta + \delta^2)\xi + \eta + (3\delta\Omega^2 - \delta^3) + i\{(\Omega - 2\delta\Omega)\xi + (3\delta^2\Omega - \Omega^3)\} = 0$$

which implies that

$$\left. \begin{array}{l} (-\Omega^2 - \delta + \delta^2)\xi + \eta + (3\delta\Omega^2 - \delta^3) = 0, \\ (\Omega - 2\delta\Omega)\xi \qquad + (3\delta^2\Omega - \Omega^3) = 0. \end{array} \right\} \quad (7.27)$$

The determinant of the coefficients of ξ and η in these equations is $\Delta(\Omega, \delta) = (2\delta - 1)\Omega$.

It may be deduced from equations (7.27) that, except when $\Delta = 0$,

$$\left. \begin{array}{l} \xi = \dfrac{\Omega^2 - 3\delta^2}{1 - 2\delta}, \\[3mm] \eta = \dfrac{\Omega^4 + 2\delta^2\Omega^2 + \delta^4 - 2\delta^3 - 2\delta\Omega^2}{1 - 2\delta}. \end{array} \right\} \qquad (7.28)$$

The non-singular locus defined by equations (7.28) as Ω increases from $-\infty$ to $+\infty$ is shown in Fig. 7.10 for the particular case $\delta = \frac{1}{4}$.

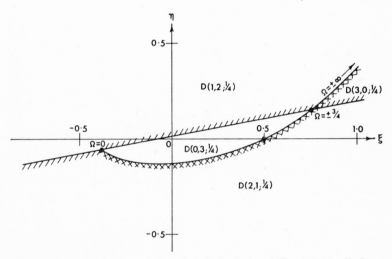

Fig. 7.10. Determination of domain of absolute stability $D(3, 0; \frac{1}{4})$ for equation 7.11.

If $\delta \neq \frac{1}{2}$, $\Delta = 0$ only when $\Omega = 0$. The corresponding singular line is found from equations (7.27) to be

$$(\delta^2 - \delta)\xi + \eta - \delta^3 = 0$$

which, when $\delta = \frac{1}{4}$, is

$$-\frac{3}{16}\xi + \eta - \frac{1}{64} = 0.$$

This line is shown in Fig. 7.10. The singular and non-singular loci are shaded in accordance with the rules given in Section 7.3.

The various domains $D(k, n - k; \frac{1}{4})$ into which the ξ, η-plane is divided can be identified by noting that equation (7.26) becomes $(S - \delta)^3 = 0$ when $\xi = 0 = \eta$, thus indicating that the origin in Fig. 7.10 lies in $D(0, 3; \frac{1}{4})$. The remaining domains can then be labelled by taking account of the shading on the D-partition boundaries. The transient response of any system governed by equation (7.11) whose representative point lies within $D(3, 0; \frac{1}{4})$ decays at least a rapidly as $e^{-t/4}$. It can be seen by comparing Figs. 7.10 and 7.6 that the domain of absolute stability $D(3, 0; \frac{1}{4})$ lies within the domain of asymptotic stability $D(3, 0)$.

If it is desired to use the method of D-partition to investigate relative stability, it is first necessary to transform the s-plane into the S-plane by the rotational transformation

$$S = e^{-i\theta}s$$

depicted in Fig. 5.4. Under this transformation the characteristic equation $F(s) = 0$ becomes

$$
\begin{aligned}
F(e^{i\theta}S) \equiv G(S) = {} & a_0(\cos n\theta + i \sin n\theta)S^n \\
& + a_1(\cos \overline{n - 1}\theta + i \sin \overline{n - 1}\theta)S^{n-1} \\
& + \ \ .\ \ \ .\ \ \ .\ \ \ .\ \ \ .\ \ \ .\ \ \ .\ \ \ . \\
& + a_{n-1}(\cos \theta + i \sin \theta)\, S \\
& + a_n = 0,
\end{aligned}
\tag{7.29}
$$

where the a_r are the original coefficients.

If the a_r are linear functions of two system parameters ξ and η, substituting $S = i\Omega$ in (7.29) will yield an equation of the form

$$
\begin{aligned}
G(i\Omega) = {} & \xi P_1(\Omega, \theta) + \eta Q_1(\Omega, \theta) + R_1(\Omega, \theta) \\
& + i\{\xi P_2(\Omega, \theta) + \eta Q_2(\Omega, \theta) + R_2(\Omega, \theta)\} = 0
\end{aligned}
$$

which implies that

$$
\left.
\begin{aligned}
\xi P_1(\Omega, \theta) + \eta Q_1(\Omega, \theta) + R_1(\Omega, \theta) = 0, \\
\xi P_2(\Omega, \theta) + \eta Q_2(\Omega, \theta) + R_2(\Omega, \theta) = 0.
\end{aligned}
\right\}
\tag{7.30}
$$

If $\Delta(\Omega, \theta) = P_1(\Omega, \theta)Q_2(\Omega, \theta) - P_2(\Omega, \theta)Q_1(\Omega, \theta) \neq 0$, equations (7.30) are non-singular and may be solved for ξ and η to give

$$
\left.
\begin{aligned}
\xi(\Omega, \theta) &= \frac{-R_1(\Omega, \theta)Q_2(\Omega, \theta) + R_2(\Omega, \theta)Q_1(\Omega, \theta)}{\Delta(\Omega, \theta)}, \\[2ex]
\eta(\Omega, \theta) &= \frac{-R_2(\Omega, \theta)P_1(\Omega, \theta) + R_1(\Omega, \theta)P_2(\Omega, \theta)}{\Delta(\Omega, \theta)}.
\end{aligned}
\right\}
\tag{7.31}
$$

When Ω increases from 0 to $+\infty$, equations (7.31) determine the non-singular locus in the ξ, η-plane corresponding to the upper sloping boundary of the region $R(\theta)$ of the s-plane shown cross-hatched in Fig. 5.3. Singular lines correspond to those positive values of Ω for which $\Delta(\Omega, \theta) = 0$ and can be found by substituting the appropriate values of Ω into equations (7.30).

It can be inferred from Figs. 5.3 and 5.4 that the non-singular map of the lower sloping boundary of $R(\theta)$ can be obtained by putting $-\theta$ for θ in equations (7.31) and then increasing Ω from $-\infty$ to 0. However, in the case of real characteristic equations it is found that

$$\xi(-\Omega, -\theta) \equiv \xi(\Omega, \theta) \quad \text{and} \quad \eta(-\Omega, -\theta) \equiv \eta(\Omega, \theta).$$

In such cases, the non-singular map of the lower boundary of $R(\theta)$ may therefore be obtained simply by tracing in the opposite direction the previously constructed map of the upper sloping boundary of $R(\theta)$. Singular lines correspond to those negative values of Ω for which $\Delta(\Omega, -\theta) = 0$.

In order to complete the D-partition boundaries corresponding to the region $R(\theta)$, it is necessary to plot the singular line $a_0(\xi, \eta) = 0$ if the coefficient of s^n in the original characteristic equation is a function of ξ or ζ. This singular locus is independent of θ.

The complete set of D-partition boundaries obtained in this way divide the ξ, η-plane into a number of domains $D(k, n - k; \theta)$ $(0 \leqslant k \leqslant n)$. For a given value of θ, $D(k, n - k; \theta)$ contains all those points which represent characteristic equations having k roots in the region $R(\theta)$ and $n - k$ roots in the remainder of the s-plane. In particular, all n roots of a characteristic equation represented by a point in $D(n, 0; \theta)$ lie in $R(\theta)$. The components of oscillatory transient response of a system governed by such an equation consequently all have damping parameters not less than $\sin \theta$. For this reason, $D(n, 0; \theta)$ is called the *domain of relative stability* θ. $D(n, 0; \theta)$ lies within the domain of asymptotic stability $D(n, 0; 0) \equiv D(n, 0)$ when $0 < \theta < \pi/2$.

This method of investigating relative stability can be exemplified by considering again equation (7.11) whose domain of absolute stability was constructed earlier in this section for the case $\delta = \frac{1}{4}$. With $S = e^{-i\theta}s$ equation (7.11) becomes

$$F(e^{i\theta}S) \equiv G(S) = (\cos 3\theta + i \sin 3\theta)S^3 + \xi(\cos 2\theta$$
$$+ i \sin 2\theta)S^2 + \xi(\cos \theta + i \sin \theta)S + \eta = 0.$$

Substituting $S = i\Omega$ in this modified characteristic equation gives

$$G(i\Omega) = (-\Omega^2 \cos 2\theta - \Omega \sin \theta)\xi + \eta + \Omega^3 \sin 3\theta$$
$$+ i\{(-\Omega^2 \sin 2\theta + \Omega \cos \theta)\xi - \Omega^3 \cos 3\theta\} = 0$$

from which it may be deduced that

$$\left. \begin{array}{l} (-\Omega^2 \cos 2\theta - \Omega \sin \theta)\xi + \eta + \Omega^3 \sin 3\theta = 0, \\ (-\Omega^2 \sin 2\theta + \Omega \cos \theta)\xi \qquad - \Omega^3 \cos 3\theta = 0. \end{array} \right\} \quad (7.32)$$

The determinant of these equations is $\Delta(\Omega, \theta) = \Omega^2 \sin 2\theta - \Omega \cos \theta$.

If $\Delta \neq 0$, equations (7.32) are non-singular and their solutions are

$$\left.\begin{aligned}
\xi(\Omega, \theta) &= \frac{\Omega^2(1 - 4\sin^2\theta)}{(1 - 2\Omega\sin\theta)}, \\[2mm]
\eta(\Omega, \theta) &= \frac{\Omega^2(\Omega^2 - 2\Omega\sin\theta)}{(1 - 2\Omega\sin\theta)}.
\end{aligned}\right\} \tag{7.33}$$

Equations (7.33) determine the non-singular loci corresponding to the upper or lower boundary of $R(\theta)$ (Fig. 5.3) according as θ and Ω are positive or negative. However, it is clear that $\xi(-\Omega, -\theta) \equiv \xi(\Omega, \theta)$ and $\eta(-\Omega, -\theta) \equiv \eta(\Omega, \theta)$ so that the latter locus is obtained simply by retracing the former in the opposite direction.

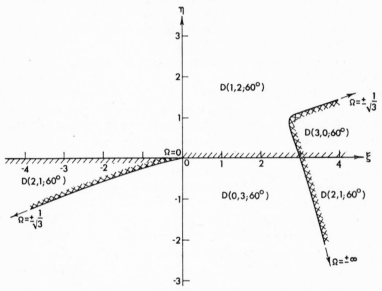

Fig. 7.11. Determination of domain of relative stability D (3, 0; 60°) for equation 7.11.

If $\theta \neq \pi/2$, the singular solutions corresponding to $\Delta(\Omega, \theta) = 0$ are found by putting $\Omega = 0$ and $\Omega = 1/(2\sin\theta)$ in equations (7.32). The singular locus corresponding to the former value of Ω is always the line $\eta = 0$, regardless of the value of θ: in fact, it is clear from equation (7.11) that a characteristic root is located at the origin of the s-plane when $\eta = 0$. The singular loci corresponding to $\Omega = 1/(2\sin\theta)$ require individual attention for each value of θ.

The complete system of D-partition boundaries for equation (7.11) is shown in Fig. 7.11 for the particular case $\theta = 60°$. The singular and non-singular loci are shaded in accordance with the usual rules. The various domains $D(k, n - k; 60°)$ can be identified by noting that when $\xi = 3$ and $\eta = 1$ equation (7.11) becomes $(s + 1)^3 = 0$. Since all the roots of this equation certainly lie within the region $R(60°)$, it follows that the point $(3, 1)$ of the ξ, η-plane shown in Fig. 7.11 lies within $D(3, 0; 60°)$. The remaining domains may then be identified as shown. The components of oscillatory transient response of any system governed by equation (7.11) whose representative point lies in $D(3, 0; 60°)$ have damping parameters not less than $\sin 60° = \sqrt{3}/2$. If Figs. 7.11 and 7.6 are compared it will be seen that the domain of relative stability $D(3, 0; 60°)$ lies within the domain of asymptotic stability $D(3, 0)$.

Problems

1. Use the method of D-partition to determine the ranges of the real parameter ξ within which systems having the following characteristic equations are asymptotically stable:

   (a) $s^3 + s^2 + s + \xi = 0$.
   (b) $s^3 + 3s^2 + (\xi + 1)s + \xi = 0$.
   (c) $(\xi + 2)s^4 + \xi s^3 + 4s^2 + 3s + 1 = 0$.
   (d) $s^3 + \xi s^2 + s + 5\xi = 0$.

   Sketch the root-loci in each case.

2. Plot the D-partition boundaries in the ξ, η-plane for the characteristic equation

   $$s^3 + \xi s^2 + \xi s + \eta = 0,$$

   where ξ and η are real parameters. Shade these boundaries by constructing the D-partition diagrams in the ξ-plane or the η-plane corresponding to the following one-dimensional cross-sections of the ξ, η-plane:

   (a) $\eta = 1$, ξ variable.   (c) $\xi = 1$, η variable.
   (b) $\eta = -1$, ξ variable.   (d) $\xi = -1$, η variable.

   Thus identify the various domains into which the ξ, η-plane is divided and compare your result with that given in Fig. 7.6.

3. Use the method of D-partition to construct the domains of asymptotic stability in the ξ, η-plane for systems governed by the following characteristic equations:

   (a) $s^3 + (\xi + 2)s^2 + (\xi + \eta - 1)s + \xi - 2 = 0$.
   (b) $\eta s^3 + (2\xi + 2)s^2 + (\eta + 1)s + \eta - 6 = 0$.
   (c) $s^4 + \xi s^3 + \eta s^2 + \xi s + 1 = 0$.
   (d) $\xi s^5 + 5s^4 + \eta s^3 + (\eta + 2)s^2 + 2s + 3 = 0$.

   In each case, ξ and η are real parameters.

4. By introducing a new variable $S = s/\Omega$ and new parameters $\xi = 2v\omega_n/\Omega$ and $\eta = (\omega_n/\Omega)^2$, show that the characteristic equation of the system described in Problem 5 of Chapter 4 can be written in the form

$$S^2 + (2i + \xi)S + \eta - 1 = 0.$$

Use the method of D-partition to construct the domain of asymptotic stability for this system in the ξ, η-plane, and thus verify that it is necessary and sufficient for asymptotic stability that $\Omega < \omega_n$.

5. A closed-loop control system with unity feedback has an open-loop transfer function of the form

$$G(s) = \frac{\xi}{s(\tau s + 1)(s + 1)} \, (\xi, \tau > 0),$$

where ξ is the open-loop gain and τ is a time-constant. Use the method of D-partition to construct the appropriate domain of relative stability if it is desired to choose ξ and τ so that the closed-loop system is asymptotically stable and has an oscillatory impulse response component with a dimensionless damping parameter not less than 0.5. Is it possible to choose ξ and τ so that, in addition, the impulse response decays at least as rapidly as e^{-2t}?

6. A whirling system consists of a mass m_1 attached to a light shaft at a point where the stiffness of the shaft in any lateral direction is k_1 and the effective internal viscous friction constant is c_1. At each of its ends the shaft runs in bearings which can be regarded as damped single-degree-of-freedom systems each having mass, stiffness, and viscous friction constants equal to m_2, k_2 and c_2, respectively. The characteristic equation of the entire system can be expressed in the complex form†

$$\alpha s^4 + 2v(1 + \alpha + \beta)s^3 + [\gamma + (1 + \alpha)(1 - 2iv\rho)]s^2$$
$$+ 2v(\beta + \gamma)s + \gamma(1 - 2iv\rho) = 0,$$

where $\alpha = 2m_2/m_1$, $\beta = 2c_2/c_1$, $\gamma = 2k_2/k_1$, $\omega_n{}^2 = k_1/m_1$, $2v\omega_n = c_1/m_1$, $\rho = \Omega/\omega_n$, and Ω is the rotational speed of the shaft. Investigate the stability of this system by the method of D-partition, and compare the effectiveness of this method with that of the generalised Hurwitz criterion in this case.

† F. M. Dimentberg, *Flexural vibrations of rotating shafts*, p. 86, Butterworths, 1961.

Chapter 8

STABILITY OF SYSTEMS GOVERNED BY DIFFERENTIAL-DIFFERENCE EQUATIONS

8.1 Introduction

The stability criteria presented in the foregoing chapters of this book concern systems governed by linear differential equations whose terms are all evaluated at the same instant of time. However, many important types of engineering system involve finite time-delays and are therefore governed by differential equations whose terms are evaluated at instants separated by finite time intervals: such equations are known as *differential-difference equations*. Thus, for example, in remote control systems incorporating telemetric links the command signal suffers a time delay in passing from the command point to the controlled system. Again, in the theoretical analysis of the chatter of machine-tools having multi-bladed cutters it is necessary to take account of the finite time interval between the cuts of successive blades. Numerous other engineering systems governed by differential-difference equations are discussed in the literature.†

Linear differential-difference equations can be written concisely by introducing the *shift operator E* defined by

$$Ex(t) = x(t + 1)$$

or, more generally, by

$$E^T x(t) = x(t + T),$$

where T is a constant. The shift operator can be expressed in terms of the differential operator $D \equiv d/dt$ by means of Taylor's theorem. Thus,

$$Ex(t) = x(t + 1) = x(t) + \dot{x}(t) + \frac{1}{2!}\ddot{x}(t) + \ldots$$

$$= \left(1 + D + \frac{D^2}{2!} + \ldots\right)x(t),$$

† See, for example, N. Minorsky, Self-excited oscillations in dynamical systems possessing retarded action, *J. appl. Mech.*, **9**, 65, 1942; R. Bellman and K. L. Cooke, *Differential-difference equations*, Academic Press, 1963.

where the dots denote differentiation with respect to t. It follows that

$$Ex(t) = e^D x(t)$$

and therefore that

$$E \equiv e^D. \tag{8.1}$$

As an illustration of the use of this notation, consider the differential-difference equation

$$m\ddot{x}(t) + c\dot{x}(t) + kx(t - T) = 0 \tag{8.2}$$

which governs the behaviour of a damped oscillator vibrating under the action of a restoring force delayed by a time T. In terms of E and D, equation (8.2) can be written in the form

$$(mD^2 + cD + kE^{-T})x(t) = 0$$

or, using (8.1) to eliminate E,

$$(mD^2 + cD + ke^{-TD})x(t) = 0. \tag{8.3}$$

Replacing D by s in (8.3) indicates that the characteristic equation of the system governed by equation (8.2) is

$$ms^2 + cs + ke^{-Ts} = 0. \tag{8.4}$$

Because of the presence of the exponential term, (8.4) is a transcendental equation having an infinite number of roots.† In fact, the characteristic equations of all linear systems governed by differential-difference equations have this property. This can be appreciated by noting that the governing equation of such a system, having a single output variable $x(t)$ and a single input variable $y(t)$, can be written in the form

$$P(D, E)x(t) = Q(D, E)y(t) \tag{8.5}$$

or, eliminating the operator E,

$$P(D, e^D)x(t) = Q(D, e^D)y(t).$$

The system transfer function is consequently

$$\frac{Q(s, e^s)}{P(s, e^s)}$$

from which it may be concluded that the characteristic equation corresponding to (8.5) is

$$P(s, e^s) = 0. \tag{8.6}$$

† This follows from the fact that the exponential function e^z is periodic; i.e., $\exp z = \exp(z + i2n\pi)(n = 0, \pm 1, \pm 2, \ldots)$.

Similarly, it can be shown that the characteristic equation of a multi-variable system governed by the set of differential-difference equations

$$\sum_{j=1}^{p} P_{ij}(D, E)x_j(t) = \sum_{k=1}^{q} Q_{ik}(D, E)y_k(t) \quad (i = 1, 2, \ldots, p) \quad (8.7)$$

is

$$|P_{ij}(s, e^s)| = 0. \tag{8.8}$$

The characteristic equations (8.6) and (8.8) both involve exponential functions and have the general form

$$F(s, e^s) = 0. \tag{8.9}$$

Since transcendental equations like (8.9) have an infinite number of roots, it is evident that the transient response of a system governed by an equation of the form (8.5) or (8.7) will in general contain an infinite number of components of the types discussed in Chapter 2. It is necessary and sufficient for asymptotic stability that the value of each of these components tends to zero as $t \to \infty$, and this will be the case provided all the roots of the appropriate characteristic equation lie in the left half of the s-plane.

Although this stability requirement is the same as that for systems governed by pure differential equations, stability criteria such as those of Routh and Hurwitz cannot be used to investigate the roots of trans-cendental equations having the general form (8.9). Nevertheless, the encirclement theorem from which Routh's criterion was derived can be used for such equations, as also can the method of D-partition. In addition, stability criteria devised by Pontryagin specifically for equations of the type (8.9) are available.

8.2 Use of the encirclement theorem: Satche's criterion

The encirclement theorem which was proved in Section 3.1 for rational algebraic functions of the complex variable s is also valid for functions of s snd e^s. Thus, if $H(s, e^s)$ is such a function,

$$N = P - Z, \tag{8.10}$$

where P and Z are respectively the numbers of poles and zeros of $H(s, e^s)$ lying within a closed contour C, and N is the number of anti-clockwise encirclements of the origin in the $H(s, e^s)$-plane as C is traversed once in the clockwise sense. It is assumed that $H(s, e^s)$ is analytic within C except for the poles and zeros, and that no poles or zeros lie on C.

This theorem can be used to investigate the stability of systems having characteristic equations of the form (8.9) by choosing the stability contour C^* shown in Fig. 3.2 as the contour C. Consider, for example, a system governed by the equation

$$\dot{x}(t) + \lambda x(t - T) = \lambda y(t), \qquad (8.11)$$

where $1/\lambda$ is a positive time constant and T is a positive time delay. It was seen in Chapter 2 that such a system is always stable in the absence of a time-delay (i.e., when $T = 0$): it will now be shown that the system can become unstable if T is made large enough.

Thus, since equation (8.11) can be written operationally as

$$(D + \lambda e^{-TD})x(t) = \lambda y(t),$$

it follows that the corresponding characteristic equation is

$$s + \lambda e^{-Ts} = 0. \qquad (8.12)$$

This can be expressed in terms of a single parameter by introducing a new variable $S = Ts$ and letting $\xi = \lambda T$. Equation (8.12) then assumes the form

$$F(S, e^S) = S + \xi e^{-S} = 0. \qquad (8.13)$$

Now on the semi-circular portion of the stability contour C^*,

$$S = re^{i\theta} \quad (\pi/2 > \theta > -\pi/2),$$

where r is infinite. It follows from (8.13) that $F(S, e^S)$ is then approximately equal to S so that the map of the semi-circular portion of C^* is itself an infinite semi-circle. The remaining portion of C^* is the imaginary axis $S = i\omega$ where $F(S, e^S)$ is given by

$$F(i\omega, e^{i\omega}) = i\omega + \xi e^{-i\omega} (-\infty < \omega < +\infty). \qquad (8.14)$$

This locus repeats itself indefinitely because of the presence of the exponential term: this is shown in Fig. 8.1 where the loci corresponding to $\xi = 1$, $\pi/2$ and 2 are plotted.

It will be noted that when $\xi = 1$ the locus does not enclose the origin so that $N = 0$ in equation (8.10). Since also $P = 0$ in the case of (8.13) it follows that $Z = 0$, i.e., equation (8.13) has no roots with positive real parts when $\xi = 1$. However, when $\xi = 2$ the origin is encircled twice in a clockwise sense so that $N = -2$ and therefore $Z = 2$, i.e., equation (8.13) has two roots with positive real parts when $\xi = 2$. Again, when $\xi = \pi/2$ the locus passes through the origin, indicating the presence of imaginary roots. It may therefore be inferred that the system governed

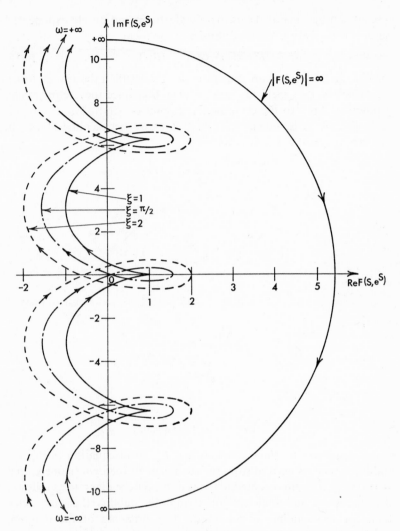

Fig. 8.1. Application of encirclement theorem to equation 8.13.

by equation (8.13) will be asymptotically stable only if $\xi = \lambda T < \pi/2$, i.e., only if $T < \pi/2\lambda$.

It will be seen from this example that even in the case of very simple characteristic equations the presence of exponential terms leads to rather complicated loci in the $F(s, e^s)$-plane. However, as Satche† pointed out, this complication can be avoided if the characteristic poly-

† M. Satche, Discussion of another paper, *J. appl. Mech.*, **16**, 419, 1949.

nomial can be separated into purely algebraic and purely exponential parts. Thus, if $F(s, e^s)$ can be written in the form

$$F(s, e^s) = G(s) - H(e^s), \tag{8.15}$$

the $G(s)$ and $H(e^s)$ loci are much simpler to plot than the $F(s, e^s)$ locus. Nevertheless, they yield the same information since the vector joining a point on $H(e^s)$ to the corresponding point on $G(s)$ obviously represents $F(s, e^s)$, as is shown in Fig. 8.2. A figure representing $F(s, e^s)$ in this way is called a *Satche diagram*.

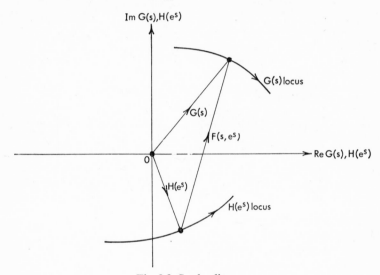

Fig. 8.2. Satche diagram.

If $F(s, e^s)$ has no finite poles so that $P = 0$ in equation (8.10), the stability criterion derived from the encirclement theorem (namely, that $Z = 0$ in (8.10)) can be stated in terms of the Satche diagram as follows: it is necessary and sufficient for asymptotic stability that the vector joining corresponding points on the two branches of the diagram suffers no change of argument as s describes the stability contour C^*. It follows immediately from Satche's criterion that asymptotic stability is indicated when the $G(s)$ and $H(e^s)$ loci neither intersect nor enclose one other, but that unstable characteristic roots exist when one locus encloses the other without intersection.

As an illustration of the use of Satche's criterion consider again equation (8.13). This has the form (8.15) with

$$G(s) = s,$$

$$H(s) = -\zeta e^{-s}.$$

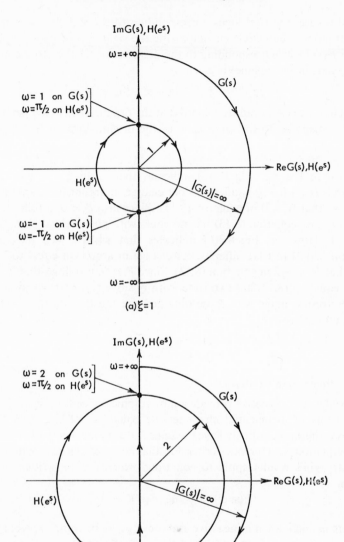

Fig. 8.3. Satche diagrams for equation 8.13.

In this case, the $G(s)$ locus corresponding to the stability contour C^* is an infinite semi-circle encompassing the right half of the $G(s)$-plane. The $H(s)$ locus corresponding to the diameter of C^* (i.e., to the imaginary axis in the s-plane) is given by

$$-\xi e^{-i\omega} = \xi e^{i(\pi - \omega)} (-\infty < \omega < +\infty),$$

which is a circle of radius ξ centred at the origin. The curved periphery of C^* maps on to the $H(s)$-plane as the origin, since $|-\xi e^{-s}| \to 0$ as $|s| \to \infty$.

The Satche diagrams for equation (8.13) when $\xi = 1$ and $\xi = 2$ are shown in Fig. 8.3. Fig. 8.3(a) indicates that when $\xi = 1$ the vector joining $H(e^s)$ to $G(s)$ suffers no net change in argument as s traverses C^*, so that $N = 0$ in equation (8.11). Since also $P = 0$, it follows that $Z = 0$, i.e., equation (8.13) has no roots with positive real parts when $\xi = 1$. However, Fig. 8.3(b) indicates that when $\xi = 2$ the vector joining $H(e^s)$ to $G(s)$ suffers a net change in argument equal to -4π, so that $N = -2$ in equation (8.13). Since $P = 0$, it follows that $Z = 2$, i.e., equation (8.13) has two roots with positive real parts when $\xi = 2$. These results agree with those obtained previously from the complete $F(s, e^s)$ locus.

8.3 Pontryagin's criteria

Pontryagin's criteria† provide a non-graphical means of investigating the roots of exponential characteristic equations of the form (8.9). These criteria accordingly have the same status in the theory of exponential equations as Hurwitz's criteria in the theory of algebraic equations. Pontryagin's results apply to equations which can be written in the form

$$F(s, e^s) = \sum_{m,n} a_{mn} s^m (e^s)^n = 0, \qquad (8.16)$$

where m and n are non-negative and the a_{mn} may be complex. Note that it may be necessary to multiply a characteristic equation by an appropriate positive power of e^s in order to bring it into this form.

If μ is the highest power of s and ν the highest power of e^s appearing in equation (8.16), the term $a_{\mu\nu} s^\mu (e^s)^\nu$ is called the *principal term* of the polynomial $F(s, e^s)$. It is important to note that not every polynomial has a principal term. Thus, although

$$F(s, e^s) = s^3 e^{2s} + s^2 e^s + 5$$

† L. S. Pontryagin, On the zeros of some elementary transcendental functions, *Izv. Akad. Nauk. SSSR*, 6, 115, 1942.

contains the principal term $s^3 e^{2s}$, the polynomial

$$F(s, e^s) = s^3 e^s + s^2 e^{2s} + 5$$

does not contain a principal term.

Pontryagin showed that a necessary condition for the stability of a system governed by an exponential characteristic equation is that the appropriate characteristic polynomial contains a principal term (when the equation is written in the form (8.16)). In fact, an exponential characteristic polynomial with no principal term has an infinite number of zeros with arbitrarily large positive real parts, and consequently represents an unstable system for all values of the coefficients a_{mn}.

The method used by Pontryagin to obtain this general result can be illustrated by considering the simple equation

$$F(s, e^s) = e^s - s = 0. \tag{8.17}$$

In this case, the polynomial $F(s, e^s)$ does not contain the principal term se^s so that, according to Pontryagin's theorem, equation (8.17) has an infinite number of roots with arbitrarily large positive real parts. The validity of this result can be demonstrated by substituting $s = \sigma + i\omega$ in equation (8.17). This yields

$$(e^\sigma \cos \omega - \sigma) + i(e^\sigma \sin \omega - \omega) = 0$$

from which it may be deduced that

$$\left. \begin{aligned} e^\sigma \cos \omega &= \sigma, \\ e^\sigma \sin \omega &= \omega. \end{aligned} \right\} \tag{8.18}$$

The first of equations (8.18) can be written in the form

$$\cos \omega = \sigma e^{-\sigma}$$

which implies that $\cos \omega \to 0$ when $\sigma \to \infty$. It follows that when σ is large the last equation has approximate solutions of the form

$$\omega = 2k\pi + \pi/2,$$

where k is a positive integer. Substituting these values into the second of equations (8.18), and then taking logarithms, indicates that the corresponding approximate values of σ are given by $\sigma = ln(2k\pi + \pi/2)$. It may therefore be inferred that equation (8.17) has roots of the form

$$s = ln(2k\pi + \pi/2) + i(2k\pi + \pi/2) + \varepsilon,$$

where $\varepsilon \to 0$ as $k \to \infty$. The real parts of such roots can obviously be made arbitrarily large by making k large enough. This confirms the validity of Pontryagin's necessary condition in the particular case of equation (8.17): the same type of proof can be used to establish the general result.

Pontryagin also obtained necessary and sufficient conditions which make it possible to test the stability of a system whose exponential characteristic polynomial contains a principal term. These conditions are usually simpler to apply than the encirclement theorem since they concern the behaviour of the polynomial $F(s, e^s)$ only on the imaginary axis and not on the semi-circular part of the stability contour C^*. Thus, in this respect, Pontryagin's criteria are analogous to Leonhard's criterion in the theory of algebraic polynomials.

Now if all the infinity of zeros of $F(s, e^s)$ lie to the left of the imaginary axis in the s-plane, the vectors joining the zeros to a point $s = i\omega$ on the imaginary axis will always rotate with positive (i.e., anti-clockwise) angular velocities as ω increases from $-\infty$ to $+\infty$. It follows that if

$$F(i\omega, e^{i\omega}) = P(\omega) + iQ(\omega), \tag{8.19}$$

so that

$$\theta = \arg F(i\omega, e^{i\omega}) = \tan^{-1}\frac{Q(\omega)}{P(\omega)}, \tag{8.20}$$

then $d\theta/d\omega$ will always be positive if all the zeros of $F(s, e^s)$ have negative real parts. Since differentiation of equation (8.20) yields

$$\frac{d\theta}{d\omega} = \frac{P(\omega)Q'(\omega) - P'(\omega)Q(\omega)}{P^2(\omega) + Q^2(\omega)},$$

where the primes denote differentiation with respect to ω, this condition can be expressed analytically by requiring that the inequality

$$P(\omega)Q'(\omega) - P'(\omega)Q(\omega) > 0 \tag{8.21}$$

is satisfied for all real values of ω. It is also evident that in such circumstances the zeros of $P(\omega)$ and $Q(\omega)$ will be real and alternating.

These are *necessary* conditions for all the zeros of $F(s, e^s)$ to lie in the left half of the s-plane. Pontryagin showed that it is *sufficient* for asymptotic stability that any one of the following conditions is fulfilled:

(i) The inequality (8.21) is satisfied for at least one value of ω, and the zeros of $P(\omega)$ and $Q(\omega)$ are real and alternating.

(ii) All the zeros of $P(\omega)$ are real and each satisfies the inequality (8.21).

(iii) All the zeros of $Q(\omega)$ are real and each satisfies the inequality (8.21).

The third of these conditions is usually the simplest to use.

Pontryagin's criteria can be conveniently illustrated by applying them to equation (8.13) which, after multiplication by e^s, has the form

$$F(s, e^s) = se^s + \xi = 0. \tag{8.22}$$

This contains a principal term so that Pontryagin's necessary condition is satisfied. Substituting $s = i\omega$ in equation (8.22) gives

$$F(i\omega, e^{i\omega}) = (\xi - \omega \sin \omega) + i(\omega \cos \omega) = 0$$

indicating that, in the notation of equation (8.19),

$$\left.\begin{array}{l} P(\omega) = \xi - \omega \sin \omega, \\ Q(\omega) = \omega \cos \omega. \end{array}\right\}$$

Now $Q(\omega) = 0$ when $\omega = 0$ or $\cos \omega = 0$. If the third version of Pontryagin's criterion is used, it is therefore sufficient for asymptotic stability that the inequality (8.21) is satisfied when $\omega = 0$ and when $\omega = \Omega$, where $\cos \Omega = 0$. This gives

$$P(0)Q'(0) = \xi > 0 \tag{8.24a}$$

when $\omega = 0$, and

$$P(\Omega)Q'(\Omega) = -\Omega \sin \Omega(\xi - \Omega \sin \Omega) > 0 \tag{8.24b}$$

when $\omega = \Omega$.

It is clear that $P(\Omega)Q'(\Omega)$ is an even function of Ω, so that only positive zeros of $Q(\omega)$ need be considered. Now $\sin \Omega = \pm 1$, since $\cos \Omega = 0$. When $\sin \Omega = -1$ it is evident from (8.24b) that

$$P(\Omega)Q'(\Omega) = \Omega(\xi + \Omega)$$

which, if $\Omega > 0$, is certainly positive when $\xi > 0$. Again, when $\sin \Omega = +1$, substitution in (8.24b) indicates that

$$P(\Omega)Q'(\Omega) = -\Omega(\xi - \Omega)$$

which, if $\Omega > 0$, is positive only when $\xi < \Omega$. Since the smallest positive value of Ω is $\pi/2$, the quantity $-\Omega(\xi - \Omega)$ is therefore positive only if $\xi < \pi/2$.

These results taken together indicate that the inequalities (8.24) will be satisfied only when $0 < \xi < \pi/2$. This condition is therefore sufficient for the asymptotic stability of a system governed by equation (8.22) and it can be shown that it is also necessary. The same result was obtained in Section 8.2 by means of the encirclement theorem.

8.4   Method of D-partition

If the coefficients a_{mn} in the exponential characteristic equation (8.16) are linear functions of one or two system parameters, the method of D-partition† described in Chapter 7 can be used to construct the domains of asymptotic stability in the parameter space. This method is often more direct than both the encirclement theorem and Pontryagin's criteria, as can be demonstrated by constructing the domain of asymptotic stability for equation (8.22).

In this case the characteristic equation can be solved for the system parameter ξ to give

$$\xi = -se^s.$$

The values of ξ corresponding to the imaginary axis of the s-plane are therefore given by

$$\xi(\omega) = -i\omega e^{i\omega} = \omega \sin \omega - i\omega \cos \omega,$$

where $-\infty < \omega < +\infty$. These values of ξ define the D-partition boundaries for equation (8.22) shown in Fig. 8.4: in accordance with the usual convention, the shading on these curves always lies to the left as ω increases. It will be noted that the D-partition boundaries spiral outwards from the origin as $\omega \to \pm\infty$, cutting the real and imaginary axes of the ξ-plane an infinite number of times in the process.

It is evident from the shading that all points lying in the domain of the ξ-plane which contains the segment $0 < \xi < \pi/2$ of the real axis must represent instances of equation (8.22) having the least possible number of unstable roots. In fact, by testing any convenient point (e.g., $\xi = 1$) by means of the encirclement theorem or Pontryagin's criteria, this domain can be identified as the domain of asymptotic stability $D(0)$. Thus, it is clear from Fig. 8.4 that if ξ is restricted to real values, all the roots of equation (8.22) will have negative real parts if and only if $0 < \xi < \pi/2$. Furthermore, if the value of ξ lies outside this interval, the real parts of an ever increasing number of characteristic roots will become positive as $|\xi|$ increases.

The construction of D-partition boundaries for exponential characteristic equations in two-dimensional parameter space can be illustrated by considering the equation

$$F(s, e^s) = s^2 + \xi s + \eta e^{-s} = 0, \tag{8.25}$$

---

† Since exponential characteristic equations have an infinite number of roots, the notation used to identify the various domains of the parameter space can be simplified. In this section, the domain corresponding to characteristic equations having r roots in the right half of the s-plane will be denoted by $D(r)$: the domain of asymptotic stability is thus $D(0)$.

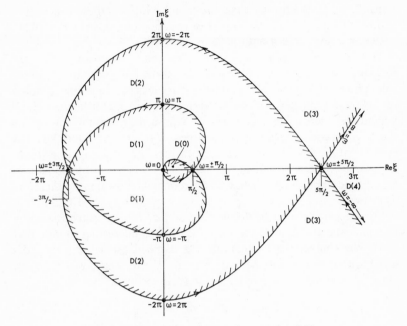

Fig. 8.4. *D*-partition diagram for equation 8.22.

where ξ and η are real system parameters. This equation satisfies Pontryagin's necessary stability condition since, after multiplication by e^s, it contains the principal term $s^2 e^s$. The first step in the determination of the *D*-partition boundaries is to substitute $s = i\omega$ in equation (8.25). This yields

$$F(i\omega, e^{i\omega}) = \eta \cos \omega - \omega^2 + i(\omega\xi - \eta \sin \omega) = 0$$

from which it follows that

$$(\cos \omega)\eta - \omega^2 = 0, \\ \omega\xi - (\sin \omega)\eta = 0. \qquad (8.26)$$

The determinant of the coefficients of ξ and η in these equations is $\Delta(\omega) = -\omega \cos \omega$.

If $\Delta(\omega) \neq 0$, equations (8.26) are non-singular and have solutions

$$\xi = \omega \tan \omega, \qquad \eta = \omega^2 \sec \omega. \qquad (8.27)$$

The formulae (8.27) determine the non-singular *D*-partition boundaries as ω increases from $-\infty$ to $+\infty$. The singular solutions corresponding to $\Delta(\omega) = 0$ are found by substituting $\omega = 0$ and $\cos \omega = 0$ in equa-

M.E.M. 1.—11

tions (8.26). In the former case, the singular locus is the line $\eta = 0$ (it is obvious that $s = 0$ is a solution of equation (8.25) when $\eta = 0$); in the latter case, ξ and η both have infinite values.

The singular and non-singular loci determined in this way have the form indicated in Fig. 8.5, where they are shaded in accordance with the rules given in Chapter 7. The non-singular locus has an infinite number of separate branches which intersect the η-axis at ordinates whose magnitudes increase as $|\omega|$ increases. The various domains into which the ξ, η-plane is divided can be identified by testing the stability of any convenient point by the encirclement theorem or Pontryagin's criteria: for example, it can be shown that the point $(2, 1)$ lies in the domain of asymptotic stability $D(0)$, and that the remaining domains are therefore as shown.

Fig. 8.5 can be used to decide the stability of any system having a characteristic equation of the form (8.25). It is interesting to note that (8.4)—the characteristic equation of a damped oscillator with a delayed spring force—can be put into this form. Thus, with $S = Ts$, $\omega_n^2 = k/m$, and $2v\omega_n = c/m$, equation (8.4) becomes

$$S^2 + 2v\omega_n TS + \omega_n^2 T^2 e^{-S} = 0$$

which has the form (8.25) with $\xi = 2v\omega_n T$ and $\eta = \omega_n^2 T^2$. It may therefore be inferred from Fig. 8.5 that a system governed by equation (8.4) which is stable when $T = 0$ can become unstable if the time-delay T is made large enough.

Differential-difference equations containing this type of delayed spring-force term are of great mechanical engineering significance since they occur in such fields as the theory of machine-tool chatter. For example, in an investigation into the chatter of vertical milling machines, Tobias[†] assumes that the equation governing the vibration of each mode of the machine-tool structure has the form

$$m\ddot{x}(t) + c\dot{x}(t) + kx = -F, \tag{8.28}$$

where the dots denote differentiation with respect to t. In (8.28), m, c and k are the equivalent mass, damping, and spring constants for the mode under investigation; F is the total exciting force arising from both chip-thickness variation and tool penetration effects and is assumed to be given by

$$F = z_e \lambda_c \left[x(t) - x\left(t - \frac{T}{z} \right) \right] + \frac{z_e \lambda_p}{z\Omega} \dot{x}(t), \tag{8.29}$$

† S. A. Tobias, The vibrations of vertical milling machines under test and working conditions, *Proc. Instn mech. Engrs*, **173**, 474, 1959.

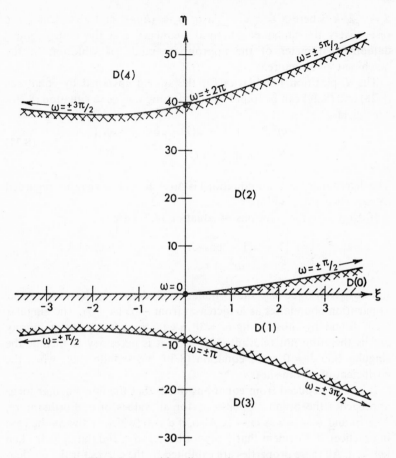

Fig. 8.5. *D*-partition diagram for equation 8.25.

where z = number of cutter blades, z_e = number of effective cutter blades, λ_c = chip-thickness variation factor, λ_p = tool penetration factor, $T = 2\pi/\Omega$ = time of cutter revolution, Ω = angular velocity of cutter, and x = relative vibration of cutter and work-piece.

If the expression (8.29) is substituted for F in equation (8.28), the characteristic equation of the resulting differential-difference equation can be written in the form†

$$F(s, e^s) = \xi s^2 + \eta s + 1 + \alpha(1 - e^{-s}) = 0. \qquad (8.30)$$

In this equation, $\xi = (z\Omega/2\pi\omega_n)^2$, $\eta = 2\nu(z\Omega/2\pi\omega_n) + (\beta/2\pi)$, and

† See B. Porter, Chatter analysis by the method of *D*-partition, *J. mech. Engng Sci.*, **7**, 348, 1965.

$\alpha = z_e \lambda_c / k$, where $\beta = z_e \lambda_p / k$. Also, $\omega_n = (k/m)^{\frac{1}{2}}$ and $v = c/2m\omega_n$ are respectively the undamped natural frequency and the dimensionless damping parameter of the appropriate mode of vibration of the machine-tool structure.

The D-partition boundaries for the system governed by equations (8.28) and (8.29) can be found by substituting $s = i\omega$ in equation (8.30). This yields

$$\left. \begin{array}{l} -\omega^2 \xi \quad + 1 + \alpha(1 - \cos \omega) = 0, \\[2mm] \omega\eta + \alpha \sin \omega \qquad\qquad = 0. \end{array} \right\} \qquad (8.31)$$

The determinant of these equations is $\Delta(\omega) = -\omega^3$ if they are regarded as equations for ξ and η.

If $\Delta(\omega) \neq 0$, the solutions of equation (8.31) are

$$\xi = \frac{\{1 + \alpha(1 - \cos \omega)\}}{\omega^2}, \qquad \eta = \frac{-\alpha \sin \omega}{\omega}. \qquad (8.32)$$

For any given value of α, the formulae (8.32) determine the non-singular D-partition boundaries as ω increases from $-\infty$ to $+\infty$. The singular locus found by substituting $\omega = 0$ in equations (8.31) lies at infinity and is therefore not relevant. However, it is necessary to include the singular line $\xi = 0$ since equation (8.30) has infinite roots when the coefficient of s^2 vanishes.

It can be deduced from equations (8.32) that the non-singular locus approaches the origin as $|\omega| \to \infty$ for all values of α. Furthermore, $\xi \to \infty$ and $\eta \to -\alpha$ as $\omega \to 0$. Also, if $\alpha > 0$ (which is always the case in practice), it is evident that ξ cannot be negative and that $\eta < 0$ when $|\omega| < \pi$. All these properties are exhibited by the curves for the particular case $\alpha = 0.5$ shown in Fig. 8.6. The various domains $D(r)$ can be identified by testing the stability of any one point (ξ, η) and then observing the number of times a shaded boundary is crossed in passing from this point to any other.

A number of interesting facts can be readily deduced from Fig. 8.6. Thus, since ξ is effectively a measure of cutter speed and since in practice $\eta \geqslant 0$, it may be inferred that the machine-tool will be asymptotically stable at all speeds greater than that corresponding to the point A, regardless of the values of v and β. In the general case, the abscissa of A is $(1 + 2\alpha)/\pi^2$, so that the system will always be asymptotically stable at speeds satisfying

$$\Omega > \frac{2\omega_n}{z}\left(1 + \frac{2z_e \lambda_c}{k}\right)^{\frac{1}{2}}.$$

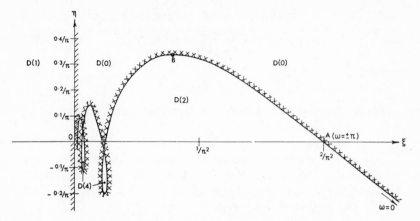

Fig. 8.6. Chatter diagram for vertical milling machine ($\alpha = 0.5$).

Again, it is evident from Fig. 8.6 that the milling machine will be asymptotically stable for all positive values of ξ if η has a value greater than that corresponding to the point B. It can be deduced from equations (8.32) that the ordinate of B is $-\alpha \cos \theta$, where θ is that root of $\tan \omega = \omega$ which lies between π and 2π. If $- \cos \theta = \rho$, it follows from the definitions of η, α and β that the system will be asymptotically stable at all speeds, and for all values of the damping parameter, provided that

$$\frac{1}{2\pi} \frac{z_e \lambda_p}{k} \geqslant \rho \frac{z_e \lambda_c}{k},$$

i.e., provided $\lambda_p \geqslant 2\pi \rho \lambda_c$.

8.5 Pure difference equations

If E is the only operator present in (8.5) and (8.7), then these equations become *pure difference equations*. In such circumstances equation (8.5) becomes

$$P(E)x(t) = Q(E)y(t) \tag{8.33}$$

and equations (8.7) assume the form

$$\sum_{j=1}^{p} P_{ij}(E)x_j(t) = \sum_{k=1}^{q} Q_{ik}(E)y_k(t), \qquad (i = 1, 2, \ldots, p). \tag{8.34}$$

Since $E \equiv e^D$ (where $D \equiv d/dt$ is the differential operator), the characteristic equations corresponding to (8.33) and (8.34) are respectively

$$P(e^s) = 0$$

and

$$|P_{ij}(e^s)| = 0,$$

which are polynomial equations in e^s having the general form

$$F(e^s) = 0. \tag{8.35}$$

Equation (8.35) is a transcendental equation whose roots can be investigated by any of the methods discussed previously in this chapter. However, if $F(e^s)$ is a rational polynomial in e^s, it is usually more convenient to introduce a new variable

$$z = e^s \tag{8.36}$$

into equation (8.35) and then examine the location in the z-plane of the roots of the resulting non-transcendental equation which will have form

$$F(z) = a_0 z^n + a_1 z^{n-1} + \ldots + a_{n-1} z + a_n = 0. \tag{8.37}$$

Because of the periodicity of the exponential function in the transformation (8.36), an infinite number of roots of equation (8.35) correspond to each root of (8.37).

Thus, for example, since the pure difference equation

$$a_0 x(t + 2) + a_1 x(t + 1) + a_2 x(t) = 0$$

can be written operationally as

$$(a_0 E^2 + a_1 E + a_2)x(t) \equiv (a_0 e^{2D} + a_1 e^D + a_2)x(t) = 0,$$

its characteristic equation is

$$a_0 e^{2s} + a_1 e^s + a_2 = 0.$$

With $z = e^s$, the last equation becomes

$$a_0 z^2 + a_1 z + a_2 = 0 \tag{8.38}$$

which has the form (8.37) with $n = 2$.

Now, in terms of s, a system governed by an equation of the form (8.35) will be asymptotically stable provided all the characteristic roots lie in the left half of the s-plane. The corresponding region of the z-plane can be found by mapping the imaginary axis of the s-plane on to the z-plane. Thus, putting $s = i\omega$ in (8.36) yields

$$z = e^{i\omega}$$

which, if ω increases from $-\infty$ to $+\infty$, defines a unit circle centred at the origin of the z-plane. Since $|z| = |e^s| < 1$ if and only if the real part of s is negative, it follows that the left half of the s-plane corresponds to the interior of the unit circle in the z-plane. Hence, a system governed by equation (8.35) will be asymptotically stable if and only if all the roots of equation (8.37) satisfy $|z| < 1$. The regions of asymptotic stability in the s- and z-planes are shown cross-hatched in Fig. 8.7.

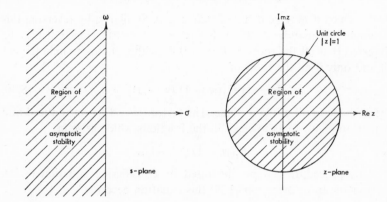

Fig. 8.7. Corresponding regions of asymptotic stability in the s-plane and the z-plane.

Numerous methods are available for determining whether all the roots of an equation of the type (8.37) lie within the unit circle. Some of the most useful of these criteria—which have found greatest engineering application in the analysis of sampled-data control systems[†]—are described in the remainder of this chapter.

TRANSFORMATION OF CHARACTERISTIC EQUATION

The problem of investigating the disposition of the roots of equation (8.37) with respect to the unit circle can be reduced to that of determining whether all the roots of a certain transformed characteristic equation lie in the left half-plane. The latter problem can then be solved by using any of the stability criteria (such as those of Routh and Hurwitz) described in previous chapters.

The required transformation of equation (8.37) can be effected by introducing a new variable w defined by

$$z = \frac{w + 1}{w - 1}, \qquad (8.39)$$

[†] See, for example, B. C. Kuo, *Analysis and synthesis of sampled-data control systems*, Prentice Hall, 1963.

where $w = x + iy$. Now if $|z| < 1$, it follows that

$$|w + 1| < |w - 1|$$

and therefore that

$$|x + iy + 1| < |x + iy - 1|.$$

This inequality implies that

$$(x + 1)^2 + y^2 < (x - 1)^2 + y^2,$$

from which it may be deduced that $x < 0$. Similarly, by reversing this argument, it may be deduced that $|z| < 1$ if $x < 0$. Hence, it may be inferred that all the roots of $F(z) = 0$ lie within the unit circle $|z| = 1$ if and only if all the roots of

$$(w - 1)^n F\{(w + 1)/(w - 1)\} = 0 \qquad (8.40)$$

lie in the left half of the w-plane. The factor $(w - 1)^n$ is introduced into equation (8.40) so as to clear all the fractions which arise in

$$F\{(w + 1)/(w - 1)\}.$$

This procedure can be illustrated by considering equation (8.38). Under the transformation (8.39) this equation becomes

$$(a_0 + a_1 + a_2)w^2 + 2(a_0 - a_2)w + (a_0 - a_1 + a_2) = 0. \quad (8.41)$$

Hurwitz's criterion indicates that all the roots of equation (8.41) will lie in the left half of the w-plane if and only if the coefficients $(a_0 + a_1 + a_2)$, $2(a_0 - a_2)$, and $(a_0 - a_1 + a_2)$ all have the same sign. This condition is equivalent to the requirement that

$$a_0^2 > a_2^2, (a_0 + a_2)^2 > a_1^2, \qquad (8.42)$$

which therefore expresses necessary and sufficient conditions for all the roots of equation (8.38) to lie within the unit circle.

It can be shown similarly that the corresponding conditions in the case of the cubic equation

$$a_0 z^3 + a_1 z^2 + a_2 z + a_3 = 0$$

are

$$a_0^2 > a_3^2, (a_0^2 - a_3^2)^2 > (a_0 a_2 - a_1 a_3)^2, (a_0 + a_2)^2 > (a_1 + a_3)^2. \,(8.43)$$

MARDEN'S ALGORITHM

Inequalities of the type (8.42) and (8.43) become rather complicated when $n > 3$, and will therefore not be quoted here. However, Marden†

† M. Marden, *The geometry of the zeros of a polynomial in a complex variable*, American Mathematical Society, 1949.

has given an algorithm which (particularly when the coefficients have numerical values) provides a ready means of investigating the roots of (8.37) when n has any value and the characteristic equation has real coefficients.

The product of all n roots of the equation

$$F_n(z) \equiv F(z) = a_0 z^n + a_1 z^{n-1} + \ldots + a_n = 0 \qquad (8.44)$$

is $(-1)^n a_n/a_0$. If these roots all lie within the unit circle, their product will be numerically less than unity so that $|a_n/a_0| < 1$. This is equivalent to the condition

$$\delta_1 \equiv a_0^2 - a_n^2 > 0. \qquad (8.45)$$

The algorithm proceeds by constructing a sequence of polynomials $F_{n-1}(z)$, $F_{n-2}(z)$, $\ldots$, $F_0(z)$ whose zeros all lie within the unit circle if those of $F_n(z)$ have the same property. In this way $(n - 1)$ conditions similar to (8.45) can be obtained.

The first step is to reverse the coefficients in the polynomial $F_n(z)$ defined in equation (8.44), thereby forming a new polynomial

$$\tilde{F}_n(z) = a_n z^n + a_{n-1} z^{n-1} + \ldots + a_0 = z^n F_n(1/z). \qquad (8.46)$$

It is then possible to determine the $(n - 1)$th-order polynomial

$$\begin{aligned} \tilde{F}_{n-1}(z) &= a_0 \tilde{F}_n(z) - a_n F_n(z) \\ &= (a_0 a_{n-1} - a_n a_1) z^{n-1} + (a_0 a_{n-2} - a_n a_2) z^{n-2} + \ldots + \delta_1 \end{aligned}$$
$$(8.47)$$

and reverse the coefficients in this polynomial to obtain

$$F_{n-1}(z) = \delta_1 z^{n-1} + \ldots + (a_0 a_{n-1} - a_n a_1) = z^{n-1} \tilde{F}_{n-1}(1/z).$$

In the same way, polynomials $\tilde{F}_{n-2}(z)$, $F_{n-2}(z)$, $\tilde{F}_{n-3}(z)$, $F_{n-3}(z) \ldots$, can be obtained. If the constant terms in $\tilde{F}_{n-2}(z)$, $\tilde{F}_{n-3}(z)$, $\ldots$, $\tilde{F}_0(z)$ are δ_2, δ_3, $\ldots$, δ_n, it can be shown that the inequalities

$$\delta_2 > 0, \qquad \delta_3 > 0, \qquad \ldots, \qquad \delta_n > 0,$$

will be satisfied if all the roots of equation (8.44) satisfy $|z| < 1$. These inequalities, together with (8.45), constitute the complete set of n necessary conditions for the asymptotic stability of any system governed by equation (8.44). It can be shown that these conditions are also sufficient.

In numerical problems the δ_r can be conveniently calculated by a tabular method rather similar to that used in connection with Routh's criterion. For example, in the case of the equation

$$F(z) \equiv F_3(z) = 12z^3 + 8z^2 - 3z - 2 = 0. \qquad (8.48)$$

the polynomials $\tilde{F}_3(z)$, $\tilde{F}_2(z)$, $\tilde{F}_1(z)$, $\tilde{F}_0(z)$ can be calculated by constructing the following array:

$$
\begin{array}{llrrr}
\tilde{F}_3(z): & -2 & -3 & 8 & 12 \\
F_3(z): & 12 & 8 & 3 & -2 \\
 & & -20 & 90 & 140 = \delta_1 \\
\tilde{F}_2(z): & & -2 & 9 & 14 \\
F_2(z): & & 14 & 9 & -2 \\
 & & & 144 & 192 = \delta_2 \\
\tilde{F}_1(z): & & & 3 & 4 \\
F_1(z): & & & 4 & 3 \\
\tilde{F}_0(z): & & & & 7 = \delta_3.
\end{array}
$$

Any coefficient in $\tilde{F}_2$, $\tilde{F}_1(z)$ or $\tilde{F}_0(z)$ (for example, the coefficient of z in $\tilde{F}_2(z)$) can be found by cross-multiplying the appropriate terms as shown, and then subtracting the resulting products. It is evident from equations (8.46) and (8.47) that this procedure correctly yields the coefficients in $\tilde{F}_{r-1}(z)$ in terms of those in $\tilde{F}_r(z)$ and $F_r(z)$. After the required value of δ_r has been noted, a polynomial may be divided by a constant factor in order to simplify the subsequent arithmetic (this has been done twice in the above example). Since δ_1, δ_2, and δ_3 are all positive in the present example, it follows that all the roots of equation (8.48) lie within the unit circle in the z-plane.

SCHUR-COHN CRITERION

Marden's criterion can be expressed as a set of determinantal inequalities analogous to those of Hurwitz's criterion: these inequalities constitute the *Schur-Cohn criterion*. This criterion applies equally to real or complex characteristic polynomials of the form (8.37).

The n *Schur-Cohn determinants* are defined by

$$
\Lambda_k = \begin{vmatrix}
a_n & 0 & 0 & \cdots & 0 & a_0 & a_1 & \cdots & a_{k-1} \\
a_{n-1} & a_n & 0 & \cdots & 0 & 0 & a_0 & \cdots & a_{k-2} \\
\cdot & \cdot & \cdot & \cdots & \cdot & \cdot & \cdot & \cdots & \cdot \\
\cdot & \cdot & \cdot & \cdots & \cdot & \cdot & \cdot & \cdots & \cdot \\
a_{n-k+1} & a_{n-k+2} & a_{n-k+3} & \cdots & a_n & 0 & 0 & \cdots & a_0 \\
a_0^* & 0 & 0 & \cdots & 0 & a_n^* & a_{n-1}^* & \cdots & a_{n-k+1}^* \\
a_1^* & a_0^* & 0 & \cdots & 0 & 0 & a_n^* & \cdots & a_{n-k+2}^* \\
\cdot & \cdot & \cdot & \cdots & \cdot & \cdot & \cdot & \cdots & \cdot \\
\cdot & \cdot & \cdot & \cdots & \cdot & \cdot & \cdot & \cdots & \cdot \\
a_{k-1}^* & a_{k-2}^* & a_{k-3}^* & \cdots & a_0^* & 0 & 0 & \cdots & a_0^*
\end{vmatrix}
$$

$$(k = 1, 2, \ldots, n) \quad (8.49)$$

where a_r^* and a_r are conjugate complex numbers. Note that Λ_k is a determinant of the $2k$th order.

If all the Λ_k $(k = 1, 2, \ldots, n)$ are different from zero and there are p sign variations in the sequence

$$1, \Lambda_1, \Lambda_2, \ldots, \Lambda_n, \tag{8.50}$$

then it can be shown† that the polynomial $F(z)$ defined in equation (8.37) will have no zeros on, and p zeros within, the unit circle $|z| = 1$. It is obvious that there will be n sign variations in the sequence (8.50) if and only if

$$\left. \begin{array}{llll} \Lambda_1 < 0, & \Lambda_3 < 0, & \Lambda_5 < 0, & \ldots, \\ \Lambda_2 > 0, & \Lambda_4 > 0, & \Lambda_6 > 0, & \ldots, \end{array} \right\} \tag{8.51}$$

It follows that all n zeros of $F(z)$ will lie within the unit circle if and only if the inequalities (8.51) are satisfied. This is the Schur-Cohn criterion.

An an illustration of the use of this criterion, consider the equation

$$F(z) = z^3 + 2z^2 + z - 2 = 0. \tag{8.52}$$

The coefficients are all real in this case so that $a_r^* \equiv a_r$. The Schur-Cohn determinants are consequently

$$\Lambda_1 = \begin{vmatrix} -2 & 1 \\ 1 & -2 \end{vmatrix} = 3,$$

$$\Lambda_2 = \begin{vmatrix} -2 & 0 & 1 & 2 \\ 1 & -2 & 0 & 1 \\ 1 & 0 & -2 & 1 \\ 2 & 1 & 0 & -2 \end{vmatrix} = -16,$$

and

$$\Lambda_3 = \begin{vmatrix} -2 & 0 & 0 & 1 & 2 & 1 \\ 1 & -2 & 0 & 0 & 1 & 2 \\ 2 & 1 & -2 & 0 & 0 & 1 \\ 1 & 0 & 0 & -2 & 1 & 2 \\ 2 & 1 & 0 & 0 & -2 & 1 \\ 1 & 2 & 1 & 0 & 0 & 1 \end{vmatrix} = -160.$$

These determinants do not satisfy the Schur-Cohen criterion (8.51), indicating that not all the roots of equation (8.52) lie within the unit circle. In fact, since in this example the sequence (8.50) is 1, 3, -16, -160 (which contains only one sign variation) it may be inferred that only one root of equation (8.52) lies within $|z| = 1$.

† See, for example, M. Marden, op. cit, pp. 148–155.

METHOD OF D-PARTITION

The method of D-partition can be used to analyse the stability of systems governed by pure difference equations by mapping the unit circle in the z-plane on to the space of the system parameters. If the unit circle is traversed in the anti-clockwise sense (so that the region of stability always lies to the left), the rules for shading singular and non-singular loci given in Chapter 7 may be used. The migration of a characteristic root from the inside to the outside of the unit circle then corresponds to crossing a D-partition boundary in parameter space from the shaded to the unshaded side.

This technique can be illustrated by constructing D-partition boundaries for the equation

$$F(z) = z^2 + \xi z + \eta = 0, \qquad (8.53)$$

where ξ and η are real system parameters. Since $z = \mathrm{e}^{i\theta}$ $(0 < \theta < 2\pi)$ on the unit circle, the corresponding loci in the ξ, η-plane are determined by

$$F(\mathrm{e}^{i\theta}) = (\cos \theta)\xi + \eta + \cos 2\theta + i\{(\sin \theta)\xi + \sin 2\theta\} = 0$$

which implies that ξ and η satisfy the equations

$$\left. \begin{array}{l} (\cos \theta)\xi + \eta + \cos 2\theta = 0, \\ (\sin \theta)\xi \quad\quad + \sin 2\theta = 0. \end{array} \right\} \qquad (8.54)$$

The determinant of the coefficients of ξ and η in these equations is $\Delta(\theta) = -\sin \theta$.

If $\Delta(\theta) \neq 0$, equations (8.54) are non-singular and their solutions are

$$\xi = -2\cos \theta, \qquad \eta = 1. \qquad (8.55)$$

As θ increases from 0 to 2π round the unit circle, the formulae (8.55) determine parametrically the segment of the straight line $\eta = 1$ lying between the limits $\xi = -2$ and $\xi = +2$. This line segment is shown with double shading in Fig. 8.8 since it is traversed from left to right as θ increases from 0 to π (when $\Delta(\theta) < 0$), and then from right to left as θ increases from π to 2π (when $\Delta(\theta) > 0$).

Equations (8.54) are singular when $\theta = 0$ or π. In the former case it may be deduced from equation (8.54) that ξ is arbitrary and

$$\xi + \eta + 1 = 0. \qquad (8.56a)$$

Similarly, when $\theta = \pi$ it is evident that

$$-\xi + \eta + 1 = 0. \qquad (8.56b)$$

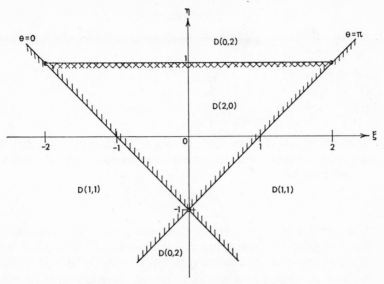

Fig. 8.8. D-partition diagram for equation 8.53.

In Fig. 8.8 the singular lines given by equations (8.56) are shaded in accordance with the usual conventions.

In this diagram, each point in the domain $D(k, n - k)$ corresponds to an instance of equation (8.53) having k roots inside the unit circle and $n - k$ outside: the domain of asymptotic stability is thus $D(2, 0)$ in the present example. This domain can easily be identified by noting that when $\xi = 0 = \eta$ equation (8.53) reduces to $z^2 = 0$ whose two roots obviously lie within the unit circle. It should be noted that, with $\xi = a_1/a_0$ and $\eta = a_2/a_0$, the inequalities (8.42) yield the same domain of asymptotic stability as is shown in Fig. 8.8.

ROOT-LOCI

If the characteristic equation (8.37) can be written in the form

$$F(z) = P(z) + \xi Q(z), \tag{8.57}$$

where ξ is a real system parameter, the rules given in Chapter 6 can be used to construct loci showing the variation of the characteristic roots with ξ. Necessary and sufficient conditions for the asymptotic stability of a system having a characteristic equation of the form (8.57) can then be determined by noting the ranges of ξ-values for which these root-loci lie within the unit circle in the z-plane.

Problems

1. Analyse the stability of time-delayed systems having the following characteristic equations:

   (a) $s^2 + 3s + 2 + e^{-s} = 0$.

   (b) $s^2 + (3 + e^{-s})s + 2 = 0$.

   (c) $s^2 e^{-s} + 3s + 2 = 0$.

   (d) $s^3 + e^{-s}s^2 + 2e^{-2s}s + 1 = 0$.

2. Transcendental characteristic equations containing exponential terms can be converted into algebraic equations of infinite degree by using the series

$$e^{ks} = \sum_{r=0}^{\infty} \frac{(ks)^r}{r!}.$$

If this series is then truncated by disregarding terms beyond a certain value of r, it is possible to examine the location of the roots of the resulting approximate characteristic equation by using any of the methods developed for algebraic equations. Investigate the validity of this approximate method by analysing the stability of a system governed by a characteristic equation which can be written in either of the following forms:

   (a) $s + \xi e^{-s} = 0$. (b) $se^s + \xi = 0$.

In each case determine the range of real ξ values resulting in asymptotically stable behaviour when $r = 0, 1, 2, \ldots, 7$, and compare these approximate ranges with the exact result.†

3. The characteristic equation of a chattering machine-tool can be written in the form

$$s^2 + 2v\omega_n s + \omega_n^2 + \alpha\omega_n^2(1 - e^{-\tau s}) = 0,$$

where ω_n and v are respectively the natural frequency and dimensionless damping parameter of the system, α is a chip-thickness variation parameter, and τ is the time between the passage of successive cutting edges of the tool through the workpiece. Solve this equation for τ and hence show that the D-partition boundaries in the τ-plane are given by

$$\tau = \frac{-\theta - i\,ln(\alpha\omega_n^2/r)}{\omega} \quad (-\infty < \omega < +\infty),$$

where r and θ and defined by

$$re^{i\theta} = (1 + \alpha)\omega_n^2 - \omega^2 + 2iv\omega_n\omega.$$

† N. H. Choksy, Time lag systems. In *Progress in control engineering*, *I*, Ed. R. H. Macmillan, Heywood, 1962.

Deduce that the D-partition boundaries intersect the Re τ-axis when ω satisfies the equation

$$\omega^4 + [4v^2 - 2(1 + \alpha)]\omega_n^2\omega^2 + (1 + 2\alpha)\omega_n^4 = 0,$$

and use this result to prove that the system will be asymptotically stable for all τ if

$$v^2 > \tfrac{1}{2}[1 + \alpha - (1 + 2\alpha)^{\frac{1}{2}}].$$

4. The relative pressure fluctuation $p(t)$ in the combustion chamber of a rocket† is governed by a differential-difference equation of the form

$$\frac{dp(t)}{dt} + (1 - \xi)p(t) + \xi p(t - T) = 0,$$

where ξ is a positive real parameter, $T = \tau/\theta$, τ is the time-delay between fuel injection and combustion, and θ is the residence time for the chamber. Show that no unstable pressure fluctuations will occur if $\xi < \tfrac{1}{2}$, but that otherwise instability will ensue if T becomes larger than some critical value T_c. Derive equations from which T_c may be determined.

5. The behaviour of a process control system‡ is governed by the equations

$$\left.\begin{aligned}
\frac{dx(t)}{dt} &= u(t) - \lambda x(t) + y(t), \\
\frac{du(t + 1)}{dt} &= -\mu x(t) - \rho\frac{dx(t)}{dt} - \sigma\frac{d^2x(t)}{dt^2},
\end{aligned}\right\}$$

where $x(t)$ and $y(t)$ are respectively the output and input of the system at time t, $u(t)$ is the value of the control signal at time t, and λ, μ, ρ, and σ are system parameters. Determine the differential-difference equation relating x and y, and hence find the characteristic equation of the system. Investigate system stability by plotting D-partition diagrams in the following cases:

(a) $\lambda = 0$, $\sigma = 0$.
(b) $\lambda = 0$, $\rho = 0$.
(c) $\rho = 0$, $\sigma = 0$.

† F. Marble and D. Cox, Servo-stabilisation of low-frequency oscillations in a liquid bipropellant rocket motor, *J. Am. Rocket Soc.*, **23**, 63, 1953.
‡ A. Callender, D. R. Hartree, A. Porter, Time-lag in a control system, *Phil. Trans. A.*, **235**, 415, 1936.

6. Analyse the stability of systems governed by the following pure difference equations. Check your result in each case by plotting the solution of the appropriate equation (in the interval $0 \leqslant t \leqslant 10$) for the stated initial conditions:

(a) $x(t + 2) + 5x(t + 1) + 6x(t) = 0$:
$x = 0$ when $0 \leqslant t < 1$; $x = 1$ when $1 \leqslant t < 2$.

(b) $2x(t + 2) + 5x(t + 1) + 2x(t) = 0$:
$x = 0$ when $0 \leqslant t < 1$; $x = 2$ when $1 \leqslant t < 2$.

(c) $2x(t + 3) + 5x(t + 2) + 7x(t + 1) - 2x(t) = 0$:
$x = 0$ when $0 \leqslant t < 2$; $x = 1$ when $2 \leqslant t < 3$.

7. At the instants $t = rT$ $(r = 0, 1, 2, 3, \ldots)$ the output $x(t)$ of a certain sampled-data system is governed by the equation

$$a_0 x_n + a_1 x_{n-1} + \ldots + a_{n-1} x_1 + a_n x_0 = 0,$$

where $x_r \equiv x(rT)$ and the a_r are constants. Show by direct substitution that

$$x_r = cz^r$$

will be a solution of this equation if z is a root of the algebraic equation

$$a_0 z^n + a_1 z^{n-1} + \ldots + a_{n-1} z + a_n = 0$$

and c is a constant. Hence show that if the last equation has n distinct roots $z_1, z_2, \ldots, z_n$, the general solution of the governing equation has the form

$$x_r = \sum_{k=1}^{n} c_k z_k^r,$$

where the c_k are functions of the initial conditions. Deduce that

$$\lim_{r \to \infty} x_r = 0$$

for any set of initial conditions if all the z_k $(k = 1, 2, \ldots, n)$ lie inside the unit circle in the z-plane.

Chapter 9

STABILITY OF SYSTEMS HAVING PERIODICALLY VARYING PARAMETERS

9.1 Introduction

The stability criteria presented in the previous chapters all relate to linear systems having *constant* parameters. However, many engineering systems have governing equations which, when linearised, assume the form

$$a_0(t)\frac{d^n x}{dt^n} + a_1(t)\frac{d^{n-1}x}{dt^{n-1}} + \ldots + a_{n-1}(t)\frac{dx}{dt} + a_n(t)x = F(t), \quad (9.1)$$

where $x(t)$ is the response variable, $F(t)$ represents external excitation, and the $a_r(t)$ are functions of *time-dependent* system parameters.

The stability of systems governed by equations of the type (9.1) cannot be investigated by the methods used for time-invariant linear systems. However, since equation (9.1) is still linear, its complete solution is the sum of any particular solution of the original equation, together with the general solution of the associated homogeneous equation

$$a_0(t)\frac{d^n x}{dt^n} + a_1(t)\frac{d^{n-1}x}{dt^{n-1}} + \ldots + a_{n-1}(t)\frac{dx}{dt} + a_n(t)x = 0 \quad (9.2)$$

obtained by putting $F(t) = 0$ in (9.1). These two components of the complete solution represent, respectively, the 'forced' and 'free' motions of the linearised system. Since the stability of a constant-parameter system was defined in terms of its transient ('free') response characteristics, it is natural to regard the variable-parameter system governed by equation (9.1) as *stable* if and only if all solutions of equation (9.2) remain bounded as $t \to \infty$.

The general theory of the stability of systems governed by equations of the type (9.2) is rather complicated when the $a_r(t)$ are arbitrary functions of time.† In any event it is commonly found that the $a_r(t)$ are *periodic* functions of time. For these reasons, much effort has been

† See, for example, R. Bellman, *Stability theory of differential equations*, McGraw-Hill, 1953.

M.E.M. 1.—12

concentrated on the task of investigating the stability of linear systems having periodically varying parameters. More specifically, extensive studies have been made of the stability of systems whose linearised governing equations have the second-order form

$$\frac{d^2x}{dt^2} + f(t)x = 0, \tag{9.3}$$

where $f(t)$ is periodic in t. Such second-order equations are known as *Hill's equations*.

It should be noted that the stability theory of Hill's equation can also be applied to equations having the form

$$\frac{d^2x}{dt^2} + p(t)\frac{dx}{dt} + q(t)x = 0, \tag{9.4}$$

where $p(t)$ and $q(t)$ are periodic in t with the same period. This follows from the fact that under the transformation

$$x = z \exp\left[-\tfrac{1}{2}\int_0^t p(t)dt\right], \tag{9.5}$$

equation (9.4) becomes

$$\frac{d^2z}{dt^2} + [q(t) - \tfrac{1}{2}\dot{p}(t) - \tfrac{1}{4}p^2(t)]z = 0,$$

where the dot denotes differentiation with respect to t. The last equation is a Hill's equation since the coefficient of z is periodic in t.

The following mechanical systems are typical of those whose stability is governed by equations of the type (9.3) or (9.4):

(i) A pendulum whose point of support is oscillated.

(ii) A torsional system which embodies a coupling (such as a universal joint) whose velocity-ratio varies periodically with rotation.

(iii) The crankshaft of a reciprocating engine whose pistons are massive enough to cause substantial periodic variations in effective crank inertia as the crankshaft rotates.

(iv) A transversely vibrating beam subjected to pulsating axial loads.

(v) A shaft running in bearings whose flexibility characteristics are unsymmetrical.

In all the above examples the differential equation in question is the actual governing equation of the system concerned, and the purpose of a stability investigation is to analyse the tendency of the linearised system to depart from a state of quiescence. However, differential equations with periodic coefficients also arise as so-called *variational equations* in the analysis of the stability of periodic motions of non-linear systems. For example, let $x_p = a \cos \omega t$ be an approximate periodic solution of Duffing's nonlinear equation

$$\frac{d^2x}{dt^2} + \alpha x + \beta x^3 = F \cos \omega t. \tag{9.6}$$

Then if this solution suffers a small variation δ, so that $x = x_p + \delta$, it may be deduced from equation (9.6) that the linearised equation governing the behaviour of δ is

$$\frac{d^2\delta}{dt^2} + \alpha \delta + 3\beta x_p^2 \delta = 0.$$

Since $x_p = a \cos \omega t$, this variational equation has the explicit form

$$\frac{d^2\delta}{dt^2} + (\alpha + \tfrac{3}{2}\beta a^2 + \tfrac{3}{2}\beta a^2 \cos 2\omega t)\delta = 0. \tag{9.7}$$

This is a Hill's equation because the coefficient of δ is a periodic function of t. If the values of a and ω are such that equation (9.7) has unbounded solutions, the motion of the system governed by (9.6) will diverge from the original periodic motion, x_p, which must therefore be regarded as unstable.

9.2 Stability theory of Hill's equation†

Since Hill's equation

$$\frac{d^2x}{dt^2} + f(t)x = 0 \tag{9.8}$$

is linear, there exists a pair of non-zero linearly independent solutions, $x_1(t)$ and $x_2(t)$, known as a *fundamental set*. These solutions have the property that any other solution of (9.8) can be expressed as a linear combination of $x_1(t)$ and $x_2(t)$, i.e., any solution can be written in the form

$$x(t) = c_1 x_1(t) + c_2 x_2(t), \tag{9.9}$$

where c_1 and c_2 are constants.

It can be shown that $x_1(t)$ and $x_2(t)$ constitute a fundamental set of solutions if and only if the Wronskian determinant

$$W(t) = \begin{vmatrix} x_1 & x_2 \\ dx_1/dt & dx_2/dt \end{vmatrix}$$

† This theory is due essentially to G. Floquet, Sur les équations différentielles linéaires à coefficients périodiques, *Ann. École N. Sup.*, **12**, 47, 1883.

does not vanish identically. A result which will be useful later can be found by differentiating $W(t)$ with respect to t. This gives

$$\frac{dW}{dt} = \begin{vmatrix} x_1 & x_2 \\ d^2x_1/dt^2 & d^2x_2/dt^2 \end{vmatrix} + \begin{vmatrix} dx_1/dt & dx_2/dt \\ dx_1/dt & dx_2/dt \end{vmatrix}.$$

Since equation (9.8) implies that

$$d^2x_1/dt^2 = -f(t)x_1$$
and $$d^2x_2/dt^2 = -f(t)x_2,$$

it follows that

$$\frac{dW}{dt} = -f(t)\begin{vmatrix} x_1 & x_2 \\ x_1 & x_2 \end{vmatrix} + \begin{vmatrix} dx_1/dt & dx_2/dt \\ dx_1/dt & dx_2/dt \end{vmatrix}$$

which vanishes since each determinant has two identical rows. Hence,

$$W(t) = W_0, \tag{9.10}$$

where W_0 is a constant which will be non-zero only if $x_1(t)$ and $x_2(t)$ constitute a fundamental set.

If the function $f(t)$ in Hill's equation (9.8) has a period of T in t, solutions $\chi(t)$ of this equation exist which have the property that

$$\chi(t + T) = \sigma\chi(t), \tag{9.11}$$

where σ is a constant. Solutions of this kind are known as *normal solutions* and play a very important role in the stability theory of Hill's equation. Now, according to (9.9), a normal solution can be expressed as a linear combination of the fundamental solutions $x_1(t)$ and $x_2(t)$, i.e.,

$$\chi(t) = \lambda_1 x_1(t) + \lambda_2 x_2(t), \tag{9.12}$$

where λ_1 and λ_2 are constants. It therefore follows from equation (9.11) that

$$\lambda_1 x_1(t + T) + \lambda_2 x_2(t + T) = \sigma[\lambda_1 x_1(t) + \lambda_2 x_2(t)]. \tag{9.13}$$

Now it can be readily verified by direct substitution that $x_1(t + T)$ and $x_2(t + T)$ are solutions of equation (9.8). These functions can therefore also be expressed as linear combinations of the fundamental set $x_1(t)$ and $x_2(t)$ by equations of the form

$$\left.\begin{aligned} x_1(t + T) &= a_{11}x_1(t) + a_{12}x_2(t), \\ x_2(t + T) &= a_{21}x_1(t) + a_{22}x_2(t), \end{aligned}\right\} \tag{9.14}$$

where the a_{ij} are constants. Substitution of these expressions into equation (9.13) yields

$$[(a_{11} - \sigma)\lambda_1 + a_{21}\lambda_2]x_1(t) + [a_{12}\lambda_1 + (a_{22} - \sigma)\lambda_2]x_2(t) = 0$$

which implies that

$$(a_{11} - \sigma)\lambda_1 + a_{21}\lambda_2 = 0, \left.\vphantom{\begin{matrix}1\\1\end{matrix}}\right\}$$
$$a_{12}\lambda_1 + (a_{22} - \sigma)\lambda_2 = 0,$$

since $x_1(t)$ and $x_2(t)$ are linearly independent and do not vanish identically. The last equations have a non-trivial solution if and only if

$$\begin{vmatrix} a_{11} - \sigma & a_{21} \\ a_{12} & a_{22} - \sigma \end{vmatrix} = 0. \tag{9.15}$$

Equation (9.15) is a quadratic in σ which has the explicit form

$$\sigma^2 - (a_{11} + a_{22})\sigma + (a_{11}a_{22} - a_{12}a_{21}) = 0. \tag{9.16}$$

Now the Wronskian of the solutions $x_1(t + T)$ and $x_2(t + T)$ defined in equations (9.14) is

$$W(t + T) = \begin{vmatrix} a_{11}x_1 + a_{12}x_2 & a_{21}x_1 + a_{22}x_2 \\ a_{11}\dfrac{dx_1}{dt} + a_{12}\dfrac{dx_2}{dt} & a_{21}\dfrac{dx_1}{dt} + a_{22}\dfrac{dx_2}{dt} \end{vmatrix}$$

which can be expanded to give

$$W(t + T) = (a_{11}a_{22} - a_{12}a_{21})W(t).$$

Since (9.10) implies that $W(t + T) = W(t) = W_0$, it follows that

$$a_{11}a_{22} - a_{12}a_{21} = 1.$$

Equation (9.16) may therefore be written in the form

$$\sigma^2 - 2\xi\sigma + 1 = 0, \tag{9.17}$$

where $\xi = (a_{11} + a_{22})/2$.

The two roots σ_1 and σ_2 of equation (9.17) define a pair of normal solutions which will be linearly independent if $\sigma_1 \neq \sigma_2$. Root-loci showing the variations of σ_1 and σ_2 with the real parameter ξ are plotted in Fig. 9.1, and it can be seen that both roots are real when $|\xi| > 1$ and complex when $|\xi| < 1$. The break-away points indicate that $\sigma_1 = \sigma_2 = +1$ when $\xi = +1$, and $\sigma_1 = \sigma_2 = -1$ when $\xi = -1$. In both these cases of equal roots, the two normal solutions are no longer linearly independent: if a normal solution is taken as one member of a fundamental

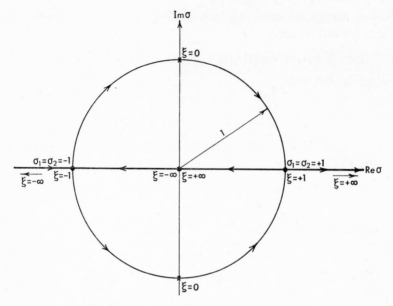

Fig. 9.1. Root-locus diagram for equation 9.17.

set of solutions, it can be shown that the other member is an unbounded function of time in such cases.†

In the first case of equal roots (when $\sigma_1 = \sigma_2 = +1$), the normal solution defined by equation (9.11) has the property that

$$\chi(t + T) = \chi(t), \tag{9.18}$$

i.e., the normal solution is periodic with period T. In the second case (when $\sigma_1 = \sigma_2 = -1$), equation (9.11) yields

$$\chi(t + 2T) = -\chi(t + T) = -[-\chi(t)] = \chi(t), \tag{9.19}$$

i.e., the normal solution is periodic with period $2T$.

Now if $|\sigma| > 1$, the corresponding normal solution defined by (9.11) increases without bound as $t \to \infty$ and is consequently unstable. Conversely, if $|\sigma| \leqslant 1$ the normal solution remains bounded and is therefore stable. It follows that the transitions from stable to unstable solutions occur when $|\sigma| = 1$, i.e., when $\sigma_1 = \sigma_2 = \pm 1$. In view of (9.18) and (9.19), it may therefore be concluded that Hill's equation has a periodic solution of period T or $2T$ at a transition from stability to instability. Periodic solutions having other periods exist, but they do not correspond to transitional behaviour.

† See J. J. Stoker, *Nonlinear vibrations*, p. 197, Interscience, 1950.

9.3 Mathieu's equation

The results given in the last section can be used to calculate the parameter values at which any particular system governed by a Hill's equation undergoes transitions from stable to unstable behaviour. This can be illustrated by considering the *Mathieu equation*, which is a Hill's equation having the form

$$\frac{d^2x}{dt^2} + (\lambda - 2\varepsilon \cos 2t)x = 0, \qquad (9.20)$$

where λ and ε are real parameters. It will be noted that the coefficient of x in equation (9.20) has a period of π in t.

In order to determine the values of λ and ε corresponding to the boundaries between stability and instability, it is necessary to obtain the conditions under which the Mathieu equation (9.20) has periodic solutions of period π or 2π. It will be shown that if the value of ε is fixed, then x has the required form when λ is equal to any one of an infinite sequence of particular numbers known as the *characteristic numbers*.

In order to calculate these characteristic numbers, it is necessary to consider periodic solutions of equation (9.20) of four types: for there can be an even (cosine) solution and an odd (sine) solution of each period (π or 2π). These solutions can be written in the following forms†:

(i)   when $\lambda = a_{2n}(\varepsilon)$, $x = ce_{2n}(t, \varepsilon) = \sum_{r=0}^{\infty} A_{2r}^{(2n)} \cos 2rt;$ (9.21a)

(ii)   when $\lambda = a_{2n+1}(\varepsilon)$, $x = ce_{2n+1}(t, \varepsilon) = \sum_{r=0}^{\infty} A_{2r+1}^{(2n+1)} \cos (2r+1)t;$

(9.21b)

(iii) when $\lambda = b_{2n+1}(\varepsilon)$, $x = se_{2n+1}(t, \varepsilon) = \sum_{r=0}^{\infty} B_{2r+1}^{(2n+1)} \sin (2r+1)t;$

(9.21c)

(iv)   when $\lambda = b_{2n+2}(\varepsilon)$, $x = se_{2n+2}(t, \varepsilon) = \sum_{r=0}^{\infty} B_{2r+2}^{(2n+2)} \sin (2r+2)t;$

(9.21d)

where $n = 0, 1, 2, 3, \ldots$. In this notation, $a_m(\varepsilon)$ is the characteristic number of the cosine-type Mathieu function $ce_m(t, \varepsilon)$, and $b_m(\varepsilon)$ is the characteristic number of the sine-type Mathieu function $se_m(t, \varepsilon)$.

Now if λ is a function of ε such that $\lambda = m^2$ when $\varepsilon = 0$, equation (9.20) reduces to the harmonic equation $d^2x/dt^2 + m^2x = 0$ when

† This notation is standard in the theory of Mathieu's equation: see, for example, N. W. McLachlan, *Theory and application of Mathieu functions*, Clarendon Press, Oxford, 1947.

$\varepsilon = 0$. It follows that when $\varepsilon = 0$ the periodic solutions of the Mathieu equation given in (9.21) must reduce to $ce_m(t, 0) = A_m^{(m)} \cos mt$ and $se_m(t, 0) = B_m^{(m)} \sin mt$, and the corresponding characteristic numbers to $a_m = m^2$ and $b_m = m^2$. Hence, if the periodic solutions and characteristic numbers are developed as power series in ε, it may be inferred that they must have the forms:

$$
\left.
\begin{aligned}
(i) \quad & ce_{2n} = \cos 2nt + \sum_{r=1}^{\infty} c_r^{(2n)} \varepsilon^r, \\
& a_{2n} = (2n)^2 + \sum_{r=1}^{\infty} \alpha_r^{(2n)} \varepsilon^r;
\end{aligned}
\right\} \tag{9.22a}
$$

$$
\left.
\begin{aligned}
(ii) \quad & ce_{2n+1} = \cos (2n+1)t + \sum_{r=1}^{\infty} c_r^{(2n+1)} \varepsilon^r, \\
& a_{2n+1} = (2n+1)^2 + \sum_{r=1}^{\infty} \alpha_r^{(2n+1)} \varepsilon^r;
\end{aligned}
\right\} \tag{9.22b}
$$

$$
\left.
\begin{aligned}
(iii) \quad & se_{2n+1} = \sin (2n+1)t + \sum_{r=1}^{\infty} s_r^{(2n+1)} \varepsilon^r, \\
& b_{2n+1} = (2n+1)^2 + \sum_{r=1}^{\infty} \beta_r^{(2n+1)} \varepsilon^r;
\end{aligned}
\right\} \tag{9.22c}
$$

$$
\left.
\begin{aligned}
(iv) \quad & se_{2n+2} = \sin (2n+2)t + \sum_{r=1}^{\infty} s_r^{(2n+2)} \varepsilon^r, \\
& b_{2n+2} = (2n+2)^2 + \sum_{r=1}^{\infty} \beta_r^{(2n+2)} \varepsilon^r.
\end{aligned}
\right\} \tag{9.22d}
$$

The above series for the ce_m and se_m have been normalised by making the coefficient of the leading term unity in each case.

The values of the coefficients $\alpha_r^{(m)}$ and $\beta_r^{(m)}$ in the series for the characteristic numbers can be found by substituting each of the pairs of expressions for x and λ given in (9.22) into the Mathieu equation (9.20). If the coefficients of the $\varepsilon^r (r = 1, 2, 3, \ldots)$ in the resulting equations are then each equated to zero, a sequence of linear differential equations with constant coefficients will be produced for the $c_r^{(m)}$ or $s_r^{(m)}$ in each case. The values of the $\alpha_r^{(m)}$ or $\beta_r^{(m)}$ can then be found by insisting that all the equations of these sequences have periodic solutions.

This technique can be illustrated by constructing the series for the periodic solution

$$
ce_1(t, \varepsilon) = \cos t + c_1^{(1)} \varepsilon + c_2^{(1)} \varepsilon^2 + c_3^{(1)} \varepsilon^3 + \ldots, \tag{9.23a}
$$

and the corresponding characteristic number

$$
a_1 = 1 + \alpha_1^{(1)} \varepsilon + \alpha_2^{(1)} \varepsilon^2 + \alpha_3^{(1)} \varepsilon^3 + \ldots, \tag{9.23b}
$$

obtained by putting $n = 0$ in (9.22b). If these expressions are substituted into the Mathieu equation, the equations for the $c_r^{(1)}$ are found to be

$$\ddot{c}_1^{(1)} + c_1^{(1)} = -\alpha_1^{(1)} \cos t + 2 \cos t \cos 2t, \qquad (9.24a)$$

$$\ddot{c}_2^{(1)} + c_2^{(1)} = -\alpha_1^{(1)} c_1^{(1)} - \alpha_2^{(1)} \cos t + 2c_1^{(1)} \cos 2t, \qquad (9.24b)$$

$$\ddot{c}_3^{(1)} + c_3^{(1)} = -\alpha_1^{(1)} c_2^{(1)} - \alpha_2^{(1)} c_1^{(1)} - \alpha_3^{(1)} \cos t + 2c_2^{(1)} \cos 2t, \qquad (9.24c)$$

and so on for $c_4^{(1)}$, $c_5^{(1)}$, ... In (9.24) the dots denote differentiation with respect to t.

It is evident that (9.24a) can be written

$$\ddot{c}_1^{(1)} + c_1^{(1)} = (1 - \alpha_1^{(1)}) \cos t + \cos 3t.$$

Its particular integral is therefore

$$c_1^{(1)} = \tfrac{1}{2}(1 - \alpha_1^{(1)}) t \sin t - \tfrac{1}{8} \cos 3t$$

which will be periodic only if the 'secular term' $\tfrac{1}{2}(1 - \alpha_1^{(1)})t \sin t$ is made to vanish by choosing

$$\alpha_1^{(1)} = 1. \qquad (9.25a)$$

In terms of equation (9.24a), this choice ensures that the coefficient of $\cos t$ is zero and consequently that 'resonance' is avoided: thus, if $\alpha_1^{(1)} = 1$, then $c_1^{(1)}$ clearly has the periodic form

$$c_1^{(1)} = -\tfrac{1}{8} \cos 3t. \qquad (9.26a)$$

If the values given in (9.25a) and (9.26a) are substituted for $\alpha_1^{(1)}$ and $c_1^{(1)}$, equation (9.24b) becomes

$$\ddot{c}_2^{(1)} + c_2^{(1)} = (-\tfrac{1}{8} - \alpha_2^{(1)}) \cos t + \tfrac{1}{8} \cos 3t - \tfrac{1}{8} \cos 5t.$$

The particular integral of this equation will be periodic only if the coefficient of $\cos t$ vanishes, i.e. if

$$\alpha_2^{(1)} = -\tfrac{1}{8}. \qquad (9.25b)$$

The particular integral is then

$$c_2^{(1)} = -\tfrac{1}{64} \cos 3t + \tfrac{1}{192} \cos 5t. \qquad (9.26b)$$

Proceeding similarly, the next coefficient $\alpha_3^{(1)}$ can be found by substituting the above expressions for $\alpha_1^{(1)}$, $\alpha_2^{(1)}$, $c_1^{(1)}$ and $c_2^{(1)}$ in equation (9.24c). The resulting equation is

$$\ddot{c}_3^{(1)} + c_3^{(1)} = (-\tfrac{1}{64} - \alpha_3^{(1)}) \cos t + \tfrac{1}{192} \cos 3t - \tfrac{1}{48} \cos 5t + \tfrac{1}{192} \cos 7t$$

which will have a periodic particular integral only if

$$\alpha_3^{(1)} = -\tfrac{1}{64}. \qquad (9.25c)$$

If (9.25c) is satisfied, the particular integral is

$$c_3^{(1)} = -\tfrac{1}{1536} \cos 3t + \tfrac{1}{1152} \cos 5t - \tfrac{1}{9216} \cos 7t. \qquad (9.26c)$$

In this way, it is possible to determine as many of the $c_r^{(1)}$ and $\alpha_r^{(1)}$ as are desired. However, if the expressions for the $c_r^{(1)}$ obtained so far are substituted from (9.26) into the series (9.23a), this becomes

$$ce_1(t, \varepsilon) = \cos t + \varepsilon(-\tfrac{1}{8}\cos 3t) + \varepsilon^2(-\tfrac{1}{64}\cos 3t + \tfrac{1}{192}\cos 5t)$$

$$+ \varepsilon^3(-\tfrac{1}{1536}\cos 3t + \tfrac{1}{1152}\cos 5t - \tfrac{1}{9216}\cos 7t) + O(\varepsilon^4)$$

which clearly has a period of 2π in t. The value of λ giving the characteristic number corresponding to this solution can be found by substituting the $\alpha_r^{(1)}$ from (9.25) into the series (9.23b). This gives

$$a_1 = 1 + \varepsilon - \tfrac{1}{8}\varepsilon^2 - \tfrac{1}{64}\varepsilon^3 + O(\varepsilon^4).$$

Power series for the other characteristic numbers associated with the Mathieu equation can be determined by the same technique. The complete set of series is found to be

$$a_0 = -\tfrac{1}{2}\varepsilon^2 + O(\varepsilon^4), \qquad (9.27a)$$

$$a_1 = 1 + \varepsilon - \tfrac{1}{8}\varepsilon^2 - \tfrac{1}{64}\varepsilon^3 + O(\varepsilon^4), \qquad (9.27b)$$

$$b_1 = 1 - \varepsilon - \tfrac{1}{8}\varepsilon^2 + \tfrac{1}{64}\varepsilon^3 + O(\varepsilon^4), \qquad (9.27c)$$

$$a_2 = 4 + \tfrac{5}{12}\varepsilon^2 + O(\varepsilon^4), \qquad (9.27d)$$

$$b_2 = 4 - \tfrac{1}{12}\varepsilon^2 + O(\varepsilon^4), \qquad (9.27e)$$

$$a_3 = 9 + \tfrac{1}{16}\varepsilon^2 + \tfrac{1}{64}\varepsilon^3 + O(\varepsilon^4), \qquad (9.27f)$$

$$b_3 = 9 + \tfrac{1}{16}\varepsilon^2 - \tfrac{1}{64}\varepsilon^3 + O(\varepsilon^4), \qquad (9.27g)$$

and, for $m \geqslant 4$,

$$a_m, b_m = m^2 + \frac{1}{2(m^2 - 1)}\varepsilon^2 + O(\varepsilon^4). \qquad (9.27h)$$

It should be noted that the last formula does not imply that $a_m \equiv b_m$ when $m \geqslant 4$, but merely that the series for a_m and b_m are then identical up to at least terms of $O(\varepsilon^3)$. In fact, $a_m \neq b_m$ when $\varepsilon \neq 0$ although $a_m \to b_m \to m^2$ as $\varepsilon \to 0$ $(m = 1, 2, 3, \ldots)$.

The series given in (9.27) (extended if necessary to higher powers of ε) can be used to calculate quite good approximations to the characteristic numbers if the parameter ε is restricted to small values. However, if ε is not small, values of the a_m and b_m obtained from power series are no longer sufficiently accurate and alternative methods of calculation (based, for example, on infinite determinants or continued fractions)† must be adopted.

Now, regardless of the method of calculation, the values of the characteristic numbers determine only the boundaries between stable and unstable behaviour. In order to identify the stable and unstable sides of these boundaries, it is necessary to use a result due to Haupt‡ which indicates that the Mathieu equation has unbounded solutions when $\lambda \leqslant a_0$ or when λ lies in any one of the infinity of closed intervals (a_m, b_m) $(m = 1, 2, 3, \ldots)$. If the characteristic numbers are plotted as functions of ε in the λ, ε-plane, it follows that the regions corresponding to unstable behaviour lie to the left of the curve representing a_0 and between the pairs of curves representing the a_m and b_m $(m = 1, 2, 3, \ldots)$. The boundary curves themselves must be regarded as belonging to the unstable regions since they correspond to the existence of equal roots of equation (9.17).

A portion of the stability chart obtained by plotting 'exact' values of the characteristic numbers is shown in Fig. 9.2, where the cross-hatched

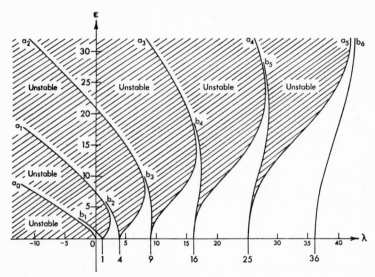

Fig. 9.2. Exact stability chart for Mathieu equation.

regions are the domains of instability. Since these domains are symmetrical about the λ-axis, the characteristic numbers have been plotted only for positive values of ε. The curves delimiting the unstable regions

† See N. W. McLachlan, op. cit.
‡ O. Haupt, Uber lineare homogene differential-gleichungen zweiter ordnung mit periodischen koeffizienten, *Math. Ann.*, **79**, 278, 1919.

diverge in pairs from the points on the λ-axis given by $\lambda = m^2(m = 1, 2, 3, \ldots)$. When m is large, it is clear that the curves constituting each of these pairs remain very close together unless ε becomes large. It may therefore be inferred that, if ε is small, the only unstable regions of sufficient width to be of practical significance are likely to be those near $\lambda = 1$ and $\lambda = 4$, together with that corresponding to $\lambda \leqslant a_0$ if λ can assume negative values.

If the parameter ε is small, these three unstable regions of the λ, ε-plane can often be delimited with sufficient accuracy by truncating

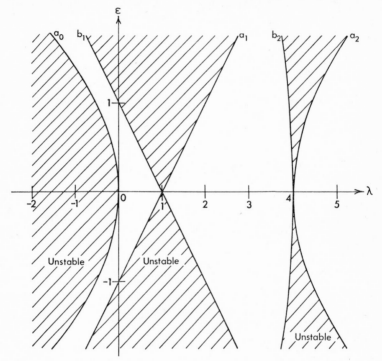

Fig. 9.3. Approximate stability chart for Mathieu equation.

the relevant power series in (9.27) after only a very few terms. Fig. 9.3 shows curves calculated from the truncated series

$$a_0 = -\tfrac{1}{2}\varepsilon^2, \qquad a_1 = 1 + \varepsilon, \qquad b_1 = 1 - \varepsilon,$$
$$a_2 = 4 + \tfrac{5}{12}\varepsilon^2, \qquad b_2 = 4 - \tfrac{1}{12}\varepsilon^2. \qquad (9.28)$$

The cross-hatched regions are the approximate domains of instability which are clearly symmetrical about the λ-axis. Comparison of Figs. 9.2 and 9.3 confirms that, if ε is small, these approximate domains are in quite good agreement with the exact domains of instability.

9.4 Illustrative example

The application of the results given in the last section to specific dynamical systems can be conveniently illustrated by analysing the stability of a pendulum whose point of support is constrained to move harmonically. Although this system has little immediate engineering importance, its stability analysis is nevertheless a paradigm of the analyses of the more complicated systems to be considered in Section 9.5.

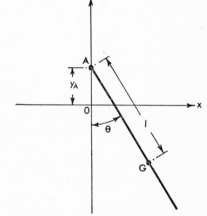

Fig. 9.4. Pendulum with oscillating support.

Fig. 9.4 shows a pendulum whose point of support, A, experiences a vertical motion given by $y_A = a \cos \omega t$. The centre of gravity of the pendulum is located at G, where $AG = l$. The mass of the pendulum is m and its moment of inertia about a transverse axis through G is equal to I. The angular inclination of the pendulum to the downward vertical at any instant is θ. If it is assumed that θ is small, the linearised equation governing the motion of this system is

$$(I + ml^2)\frac{d^2\theta}{dt^2} + ml(g + \ddot{y}_A)\theta = 0.$$

This can be written in the form

$$\frac{d^2\theta}{dt^2} + \omega_n^2\left(1 + \frac{\ddot{y}_A}{g}\right)\theta = 0,$$

where ω_n is the undamped natural frequency of small oscillations of the pendulum given by $\omega_n^2 = mgl/(I + ml^2)$. Since $\ddot{y}_A = -\omega^2 a \cos \omega t$, the last equation has the explicit form

$$\frac{d^2\theta}{dt^2} + \omega_n^2\left(1 - \frac{\omega^2 a}{g} \cos \omega t\right)\theta = 0. \tag{9.29}$$

Now although the coefficient of θ in equation (9.29) is a periodic function of t, this equation is not in the standard form (9.20) of Mathieu's equation since the period of the coefficient is $2\pi/\omega$ rather than π. However, if a new time variable $\tau = \omega t/2$ is introduced, equation (9.29) becomes

$$\frac{d^2\theta}{d\tau^2} + \left(\frac{4\omega_n^2}{\omega^2} - \frac{4a\omega_n^2}{g} \cos 2\tau\right)\theta = 0. \tag{9.30}$$

This is a Mathieu equation with

$$\lambda = \frac{4\omega_n^2}{\omega^2}, \qquad \varepsilon = \frac{2a\omega_n^2}{g}, \tag{9.31}$$

and it is evident that the solutions of (9.30) will be unstable if and only if the corresponding solutions of (9.29) are unstable.

The stability charts given in Section 9.3 may therefore be used to investigate the stability of the pendulum. Since λ and ε as defined in (9.31) cannot be negative, only the first quadrant of Fig. 9.2 is relevant to the present analysis. If $\varepsilon = 0$ (i.e., if the support point is not oscillated), the motions of the pendulum are the steady bounded oscillations given by the solutions of the harmonic equation $d^2\theta/dt^2 + \omega_n^2\theta = 0$ to which (9.29) reduces when $a = 0$. However, if the support point is oscillated, ε becomes positive and Fig. 9.2 indicates that there is then an infinite number of ranges of λ within which equation (9.29) has unbounded solutions. If ω (the frequency of oscillation of the support point) is gradually increased from zero, it is evident from the definition given in (9.31) that the value of λ will be correspondingly decreased from $+\infty$. Thus, if ε has a fixed value, it may be inferred from Fig. 9.2 that ranges of frequency giving rise to stable motions alternate with unstable ranges, the latter ranges becoming wider as the frequency ω is increased.

If ε is small, the unstable frequency ranges lie near the values $\lambda = m^2$ ($m = 1, 2, 3, \ldots$), i.e., near the frequencies $\omega = 2\omega_n/m$ ($m = 1, 2, 3, \ldots$). However, when ε is small it is also clear from Fig. 9.2 that the only unstable frequency ranges of appreciable width are those delimited by the two pairs of characteristic numbers (a_1, b_1) and (a_2, b_2), i.e., those lying near the frequencies $\omega = 2\omega_n$, $\omega = \omega_n$. In this case the approximate stability chart shown in Fig. 9.3 may be used. This chart indicates that the principal frequency ranges of instability are given approximately by

$$+ \tfrac{5}{12}\left(\frac{2a\omega_n^2}{g}\right)^2 > \frac{4\omega_n^2}{\omega^2} > 4 - \tfrac{1}{12}\left(\frac{2a\omega_n^2}{g}\right)^2 \qquad (9.32a)$$

and

$$1 + \left(\frac{2a\omega_n^2}{g}\right) > \frac{\omega_n^2}{\omega^2} > 1 - \left(\frac{2a\omega_n^2}{g}\right). \qquad (9.32b)$$

For example, if $2a\omega_n^2/g = 0.5$ and $\omega_n = 100$ rad/sec, the frequency ranges of instability defined by (9.32a) and (9.32b) are 100.26 rad/sec $> \omega > 98.72$ rad/sec and 282.84 rad/sec $> \omega > 163.30$ rad/sec respectively.

In interpreting these results it is important to recall that equation (9.29) is an approximate linearised equation of motion which ceases to be valid when θ becomes large. Now according to the foregoing stability analysis based on this linearised equation, the pendulum will depart further and further from its equilibrium position after a disturbance if its support point is oscillated in such a way that the relevant values of λ and ε lie in an unstable region of the λ, ε-plane. However, because the nonlinearity of the system cannot be ignored when θ is large, in such circumstances the motion of the pendulum will not increase without bound but will in fact eventually settle into a limit cycle of oscillation having a large amplitude. The linearised analysis must obviously be abandoned if realistic predictions of the amplitude of this limit cycle are required. However, if it is desired to predict only the conditions under which oscillations of large amplitude can occur, the domains of instability obtained from the linearised theory are usually sufficiently accurate.

The stability theory of Mathieu's equation has so far been used to show that there are certain ranges within which the position of stable equilibrium ($\theta = 0$) of a pendulum can become unstable. It is interesting to note that the same theory can be used to demonstrate the existence of a frequency range within which the position of unstable equilibrium ($\theta = \pi$) of the pendulum can be *stabilised* as a result of the oscillations of the support point. Thus, if ϕ denotes a small departure of the pendulum from the position $\theta = \pi$, equation (9.29) becomes

$$\frac{d^2\phi}{dt^2} - \omega_n^2\left(1 - \frac{\omega^2 a}{g}\cos\omega t\right)\phi = 0 \qquad (9.33)$$

which assumes the form

$$\frac{d^2\phi}{d\tau^2} + \left(-\frac{4\omega_n^2}{\omega^2} + \frac{4a\omega_n^2}{g}\cos 2\tau\right)\phi = 0 \qquad (9.34)$$

if a new time variable $\tau = \omega t/2$ is introduced, as before. The last equation is a Mathieu equation of the standard form (9.20) with

$$\lambda = -\frac{4\omega_n^2}{\omega^2}, \qquad \varepsilon = -\frac{2a\omega_n^2}{g}. \qquad (9.35)$$

Since λ and ε now cannot be positive, only the third quadrant of the stability chart is relevant to the problem of the inverted pendulum. Moreover, since the whole of the negative λ-axis lies in a domain of instability, Fig. 9.2 agrees with the known result that the inverted position of equilibrium of the pendulum is unstable when $\varepsilon = 0$, i.e., when the support point of the pendulum is stationary. However, if the point of support is oscillated, ε becomes negative and Fig. 9.2 indicates that the inverted pendulum can be stabilised by making the frequency ω high enough to satisfy $\lambda > a_0$.

In terms of the approximate stability boundaries plotted in Fig. 9.3, this inequality is simply $\lambda > -\frac{1}{2}\varepsilon^2$. It follows from (9.35) that, for stability, ω must be high enough to satisfy the approximate inequality

$$\frac{4\omega_n^2}{\omega^2} < \frac{1}{2}\left(\frac{2a\omega_n^2}{g}\right)^2. \qquad (9.36a)$$

But, if $\varepsilon < -1$, it is also evident from Fig. 9.3 that if ω is increased beyond the value required by (9.36a) the inverted pendulum will eventually become unstable again. This will happen when ω is high enough to satisfy $\lambda > a_1$, i.e., when $\lambda > 1 + \varepsilon$, approximately. In terms of the parameters defined in (9.35), this inequality indicates that the pendulum will be unstable at all frequencies satisfying

$$\frac{4\omega_n^2}{\omega^2} < \frac{2a\omega_n^2}{g} - 1 \qquad (9.36b)$$

if $2a\omega_n^2/g > 1$.

In the case of the previously discussed numerical example for which $2a\omega_n^2/g = 0\cdot5$ and $\omega_n = 100$ rad/sec, the inequality (9.36a) gives $\omega > 565\cdot66$ rad/sec as the necessary condition for stability. Since $\varepsilon = -0\cdot5 \nless -1$, this result implies that the inverted pendulum will be stable at all frequencies greater than $565\cdot66$ rad/sec. However, if for example $2a\omega_n^2/g = -\varepsilon = 1\cdot5$, the inequality (9.36b) applies, and the two inequalities (9.36) taken together indicate that the inverted pendulum will then be stable only in the approximate frequency range $282\cdot85$ rad/sec $> \omega > 188\cdot55$ rad/sec.

9.5 Generalised Mathieu equation

It has been shown[†] that the stability of a number of engineering systems possessing periodically varying parameters is governed by a Hill's equation having the special form

$$\frac{d^2x}{dt^2} + \left[\lambda \left\{ 1 + \sum_{r=1}^{\infty} \varepsilon^r \left(\sum_{s=0}^{r} \mu_{rs} \cos 2st \right) \right\} + \right.$$

$$\left. \sum_{r=1}^{\infty} \varepsilon^r \left(\sum_{s=0}^{r} v_{rs} \cos 2st \right) \right] x = 0, \quad (9.37)$$

where the μ_{rs} and v_{rs} are system parameters. Since this equation reduces to the Mathieu equation when $v_{11} = -2$ and the rest of the μ_{rs} and v_{rs} are zero, it can be regarded as a generalised Mathieu equation. The coefficient of x in equation (9.37) has a period of π in t, as in the case of Mathieu's equation.

Since (9.37) is a Hill's equation, the results given in Section 9.2 indicate that the transitions from stable to unstable behaviour occur whenever λ is related to ε and the μ_{rs} and v_{rs} in such a way that equation (9.37) has a periodic solution of period π or 2π in t. These particular values of λ are again called the characteristic numbers of the corresponding periodic solutions and will be denoted by $\tilde{a}_m$ and $\tilde{b}_m$, the tildes serving to prevent confusion between the characteristic numbers for equation (9.37) and the corresponding quantities for Mathieu's equation. In this notation the results of Haupt referred to in Section 9.3 can be stated as follows: for any particular system, having fixed values of ε and the μ_{rs} and v_{rs}, the linearised equation (9.37) has unbounded solutions whenever $\lambda \leqslant \tilde{a}_0$ or λ lies in any one of the closed intervals $(\tilde{a}_m, \tilde{b}_m)$ $(m = 1, 2, 3, \ldots)$.

The characteristic numbers $\tilde{a}_m$ and $\tilde{b}_m$ can be developed as power series in ε by precisely the same method as was used for the Mathieu equation in Section 9.3. The coefficients in these power series are functions of the μ_{rs} and v_{rs}, and so the approximate stability boundaries for any particular system can be obtained by assigning the appropriate values to the μ_{rs} and v_{rs} in the general power series. These series have the following forms:

$$\tilde{a}_0 = (-v_{10})\varepsilon + (\mu_{10}v_{10} - \tfrac{1}{8}v_{11}^2 - v_{20})\varepsilon^2 + (-\mu_{10}^2v_{10} + \tfrac{1}{8}\mu_{10}v_{11}^2 + \mu_{10}v_{20} + \tfrac{1}{4}\mu_{11}v_{10}v_{11} + \mu_{20}v_{10} - \tfrac{1}{4}v_{11}v_{21} - v_{30})\varepsilon^3 + O(\varepsilon^4), \quad (9.38a)$$

† B. Porter, The stability of systems governed by a special form of Hill's equation, *Int. J. mech. Sci.*, **4**, 313, 1962.

$$\begin{aligned}
\tilde{a}_1 = 1 &+ (-\mu_{10} - \tfrac{1}{2}\mu_{11} - \nu_{10} - \tfrac{1}{2}\nu_{11})\varepsilon + (\mu_{10}^2 + \mu_{10}\mu_{11} \\
&+ \mu_{10}\nu_{10} + \tfrac{1}{2}\mu_{10}\nu_{11} + \tfrac{7}{32}\mu_{11}^2 + \tfrac{1}{2}\mu_{11}\nu_{10} + \tfrac{3}{16}\mu_{11}\nu_{11} \\
&- \mu_{20} - \tfrac{1}{2}\mu_{21} - \tfrac{1}{32}\nu_{11}^2 - \nu_{20} - \tfrac{1}{2}\nu_{21})\varepsilon^2 + (-\mu_{10}^3 \\
&- \tfrac{3}{2}\mu_{10}^2\mu_{11} - \tfrac{21}{32}\mu_{10}\mu_{11}^2 + 2\mu_{10}\mu_{20} + \mu_{10}\mu_{21} - \mu_{10}^2\nu_{10} \\
&- \tfrac{1}{2}\mu_{10}^2\nu_{11} + \tfrac{1}{32}\mu_{10}\nu_{11}^2 + \mu_{10}\nu_{20} + \tfrac{1}{2}\mu_{10}\nu_{21} - \mu_{10}\mu_{11}\nu_{10} \\
&- \tfrac{3}{8}\mu_{10}\mu_{11}\nu_{11} - \tfrac{39}{512}\mu_{11}^3 + \mu_{11}\mu_{20} + \tfrac{7}{16}\mu_{11}\mu_{21} \\
&- \tfrac{1}{16}\mu_{11}\mu_{22} - \tfrac{3}{16}\mu_{11}^2\nu_{10} - \tfrac{13}{512}\mu_{11}^2\nu_{11} + \tfrac{27}{512}\mu_{11}\nu_{11}^2 \\
&+ \tfrac{1}{2}\mu_{11}\nu_{20} + \tfrac{3}{16}\mu_{11}\nu_{21} - \tfrac{1}{16}\mu_{11}\nu_{22} + \tfrac{1}{16}\mu_{11}\nu_{10}\nu_{11} \\
&+ \mu_{20}\nu_{10} + \tfrac{1}{2}\mu_{20}\nu_{11} + \tfrac{1}{2}\mu_{21}\nu_{10} + \tfrac{1}{16}\mu_{21}\nu_{11} - \tfrac{1}{16}\mu_{22}\nu_{11} \\
&- \mu_{30} - \tfrac{1}{2}\mu_{31} + \tfrac{1}{512}\nu_{11}^3 - \tfrac{1}{16}\nu_{11}\nu_{21} - \tfrac{1}{16}\nu_{11}\nu_{22} \\
&- \nu_{30} - \tfrac{1}{2}\nu_{31})\varepsilon^3 + O(\varepsilon^4), \tag{9.38b}
\end{aligned}$$

$$\begin{aligned}
\tilde{b}_1 = 1 &+ (-\mu_{10} + \tfrac{1}{2}\mu_{11} - \nu_{10} + \tfrac{1}{2}\nu_{11})\varepsilon + (\mu_{10}^2 - \mu_{10}\mu_{11} \\
&+ \mu_{10}\nu_{10} - \tfrac{1}{2}\mu_{10}\nu_{11} + \tfrac{7}{32}\mu_{11}^2 - \tfrac{1}{2}\mu_{11}\nu_{10} + \tfrac{3}{16}\mu_{11}\nu_{11} \\
&- \mu_{20} + \tfrac{1}{2}\mu_{21} - \tfrac{1}{32}\nu_{11}^2 - \nu_{20} + \tfrac{1}{2}\nu_{21})\varepsilon^2 + (-\mu_{10}^3 \\
&+ \tfrac{3}{2}\mu_{10}^2\mu_{11} - \tfrac{21}{32}\mu_{10}\mu_{11}^2 + 2\mu_{10}\mu_{20} - \mu_{10}\mu_{21} - \mu_{10}^2\nu_{10} \\
&+ \tfrac{1}{2}\mu_{10}^2\nu_{11} + \tfrac{1}{32}\mu_{10}\nu_{11} + \mu_{10}\nu_{20} - \tfrac{1}{2}\mu_{10}\nu_{21} \\
&+ \mu_{10}\mu_{11}\nu_{10} - \tfrac{3}{8}\mu_{10}\mu_{11}\nu_{11} + \tfrac{39}{512}\mu_{11}^3 - \mu_{11}\mu_{20} \\
&+ \tfrac{7}{16}\mu_{11}\mu_{21} + \tfrac{1}{16}\mu_{11}\mu_{22} - \tfrac{3}{16}\mu_{11}^2\nu_{10} + \tfrac{13}{512}\mu_{11}^2\nu_{11} \\
&- \tfrac{27}{512}\mu_{11}\nu_{11}^2 - \tfrac{1}{2}\mu_{11}\nu_{20} + \tfrac{3}{16}\mu_{11}\nu_{21} + \tfrac{1}{16}\mu_{11}\nu_{22} \\
&+ \tfrac{1}{16}\mu_{11}\nu_{10}\nu_{11} + \mu_{20}\nu_{10} - \tfrac{1}{2}\mu_{20}\nu_{11} - \tfrac{1}{2}\mu_{21}\nu_{10} \\
&+ \tfrac{3}{16}\mu_{21}\nu_{11} + \tfrac{1}{16}\mu_{22}\nu_{11} - \mu_{30} + \tfrac{1}{2}\mu_{31} - \tfrac{1}{512}\nu_{11}^3 \\
&- \tfrac{1}{16}\nu_{11}\nu_{21} + \tfrac{1}{16}\nu_{11}\nu_{22} - \nu_{30} + \tfrac{1}{2}\nu_{31})\varepsilon^3 + O(\varepsilon^4), \tag{9.38c}
\end{aligned}$$

$$\begin{aligned}
\tilde{a}_2 = 4 &+ (-4\mu_{10} - \nu_{10})\varepsilon + (4\mu_{10}^2 + \mu_{10}\nu_{10} + \tfrac{5}{3}\mu_{11}^2 + \tfrac{5}{6}\mu_{11}\nu_{11} \\
&- 4\mu_{20} - 2\mu_{22} + \tfrac{5}{48}\nu_{11}^2 - \nu_{20} - \tfrac{1}{2}\nu_{22})\varepsilon^2 + (-4\mu_{10}^3 \\
&- \mu_{10}^2\nu_{10} - 5\mu_{10}\mu_{11}^2 - \tfrac{5}{3}\mu_{10}\mu_{11}\nu_{11} + 8\mu_{10}\mu_{20} + 4\mu_{10}\mu_{22} \\
&- \tfrac{5}{48}\mu_{10}\nu_{11}^2 + \mu_{10}\nu_{20} + \tfrac{1}{2}\mu_{10}\nu_{22} + \tfrac{10}{3}\mu_{11}\mu_{21} - \tfrac{5}{6}\mu_{11}^2\nu_{10} \\
&+ \tfrac{5}{6}\mu_{11}\nu_{21} - \tfrac{5}{24}\mu_{11}\nu_{10}\nu_{11} + \mu_{20}\nu_{10} + \tfrac{5}{6}\mu_{21}\nu_{11} + \tfrac{1}{2}\mu_{22}\nu_{10} \\
&- 4\mu_{30} - 2\mu_{32} + \tfrac{5}{24}\nu_{11}\nu_{21} - \nu_{30} - \tfrac{1}{2}\nu_{32})\varepsilon^3 + O(\varepsilon^4), \\
&\hspace{8cm} \tag{9.38d}
\end{aligned}$$

$$\begin{aligned}
\tilde{b}_2 = 4 &+ (-4\mu_{10} - \nu_{10})\varepsilon + (4\mu_{10}^2 + \mu_{10}\nu_{10} - \tfrac{1}{3}\mu_{11}^2 - \tfrac{1}{6}\mu_{11}\nu_{11} \\
&- 4\mu_{20} + 2\mu_{22} - \tfrac{1}{48}\nu_{11}^2 - \nu_{20} + \tfrac{1}{2}\nu_{22})\varepsilon^2 + (-4\mu_{10}^3 \\
&- \mu_{10}^2\nu_{10} + \mu_{10}\mu_{11}^2 + \tfrac{1}{3}\mu_{10}\mu_{11}\nu_{11} + 8\mu_{10}\mu_{20} - 4\mu_{10}\mu_{22} \\
&+ \tfrac{1}{48}\mu_{10}\nu_{11}^2 + \mu_{10}\nu_{20} - \tfrac{1}{2}\mu_{10}\nu_{22} + \tfrac{1}{6}\mu_{11}^2\nu_{10} - \tfrac{2}{3}\mu_{11}\mu_{21} \\
&- \tfrac{1}{6}\mu_{11}\nu_{21} + \tfrac{1}{24}\mu_{11}\nu_{10}\nu_{11} + \mu_{20}\nu_{10} - \tfrac{1}{6}\mu_{21}\nu_{11} \\
&- \tfrac{1}{2}\mu_{22}\nu_{10} - 4\mu_{30} + 2\mu_{32} - \tfrac{1}{24}\nu_{11}\nu_{21} - \nu_{30} \\
&+ \tfrac{1}{2}\nu_{32})\varepsilon^3 + O(\varepsilon^4), \tag{9.38e}
\end{aligned}$$

$$\begin{aligned}
\tilde{a}_3 = 9 &+ (-9\mu_{10} - \nu_{10})\varepsilon + (9\mu_{10}^2 + \mu_{10}\nu_{10} + \tfrac{81}{64}\mu_{11}^2 \\
&+ \tfrac{9}{32}\mu_{11}\nu_{11} - 9\mu_{20} + \tfrac{1}{64}\nu_{11}^2 - \nu_{20})\varepsilon^2 + (-9\mu_{10}^3 \\
&- \mu_{10}^2\nu_{10} - \tfrac{243}{64}\mu_{10}\mu_{11}^2 - \tfrac{9}{16}\mu_{10}\mu_{11}\nu_{11} + 18\mu_{10}\mu_{20} \\
&- \tfrac{1}{64}\mu_{10}\nu_{11}^2 + \mu_{10}\nu_{20} - \tfrac{729}{512}\mu_{11}^3 - \tfrac{243}{512}\mu_{11}^2\nu_{11}
\end{aligned}$$

$$- \tfrac{9}{32}\mu_{11}^2 v_{10} + \tfrac{81}{32}\mu_{11}\mu_{21} + \tfrac{81}{16}\mu_{11}\mu_{22} - \tfrac{27}{512}\mu_{11}v_{11}^2$$

$$+ \tfrac{9}{32}\mu_{11}v_{21} + \tfrac{9}{16}\mu_{11}v_{22} - \tfrac{1}{32}\mu_{11}v_{10}v_{11} + \mu_{20}v_{10}$$

$$+ \tfrac{9}{32}\mu_{21}v_{11} + \tfrac{9}{16}\mu_{22}v_{11} - 9\mu_{30} - \tfrac{9}{2}\mu_{33} - \tfrac{1}{512}v_{11}^3$$

$$+ \tfrac{1}{32}v_{11}v_{21} + \tfrac{1}{16}v_{11}v_{22} - v_{30} - \tfrac{1}{2}v_{33})\varepsilon^3 + O(\varepsilon^4), \quad (9.38f)$$

$$\tilde{b}_3 = 9 + (-9\mu_{10} - v_{10})\varepsilon + (9\mu_{10}^2 + \mu_{10}v_{10} + \tfrac{81}{64}\mu_{11}^2$$

$$+ \tfrac{9}{32}\mu_{11}v_{11} - 9\mu_{20} + \tfrac{1}{64}v_{11}^2 - v_{20})\varepsilon^2 + (-9\mu_{10}^3$$

$$- \mu_{10}^2 v_{10} - \tfrac{243}{64}\mu_{10}\mu_{11}^2 - \tfrac{9}{16}\mu_{10}\mu_{11}v_{11} + 18\mu_{10}\mu_{20}$$

$$- \tfrac{1}{64}\mu_{10}v_{11}^2 + \mu_{10}v_{20} + \tfrac{729}{512}\mu_{11}^3 + \tfrac{243}{512}\mu_{11}^2 v_{11}$$

$$- \tfrac{9}{32}\mu_{11}^2 v_{10} + \tfrac{81}{32}\mu_{11}\mu_{21} - \tfrac{81}{16}\mu_{11}\mu_{22} + \tfrac{27}{512}\mu_{11}v_{11}^2$$

$$+ \tfrac{9}{32}\mu_{11}v_{21} - \tfrac{9}{16}\mu_{11}v_{22} - \tfrac{1}{32}\mu_{11}v_{10}v_{11} + \mu_{20}v_{10}$$

$$+ \tfrac{9}{32}\mu_{21}v_{11} - \tfrac{9}{16}\mu_{22}v_{11} - 9\mu_{30} + \tfrac{9}{2}\mu_{33} + \tfrac{1}{512}v_{11}^3$$

$$+ \tfrac{1}{32}v_{11}v_{21} - \tfrac{1}{16}v_{11}v_{22} - v_{30} + \tfrac{1}{2}v_{33})\varepsilon^3 + O(\varepsilon^4), \quad (9.38g)$$

and, for $m \geqslant 4$,

$$\tilde{a}_m, \tilde{b}_m, = m^2 + (-m^2\mu_{10} - v_{10})\varepsilon + \{m^2\mu_{10}^2 + \mu_{10}v_{10}$$

$$+ \frac{m^4}{8(m^2 - 1)}\mu_{11}^2 + \frac{m^2}{4(m^2 - 1)}\mu_{11}v_{11} - m^2\mu_{20}$$

$$+ \frac{1}{8(m^2 - 1)}v_{11}^2 - v_{20}\}\varepsilon^2 + \{-m^2\mu_{10}^3$$

$$- \frac{3m^4}{8(m^2 - 1)}\mu_{10}\mu_{11}^2 + 2m^2\mu_{10}\mu_{20} - \mu_{10}^2 v_{10}$$

$$- \frac{m^2}{2(m^2 - 1)}\mu_{10}\mu_{11}v_{11} - \frac{1}{8(m^2 - 1)}\mu_{10}v_{11}^2 + \mu_{10}v_{20}$$

$$+ \frac{m^4}{4(m^2 - 1)}\mu_{11}\mu_{21} - \frac{m^2}{4(m^2 - 1)}\mu_{11}^2 v_{10}$$

$$- \frac{1}{4(m^2 - 1)}\mu_{11}v_{10}v_{11} + \frac{m^2}{4(m^2 - 1)}\mu_{11}v_{21} + \mu_{20}v_{10}$$

$$+ \frac{m^2}{4(m^2 - 1)}\mu_{21}v_{11} - m^2\mu_{30} + \frac{1}{4(m^2 - 1)}v_{11}v_{21}$$

$$- v_{30}\}\varepsilon^3 + O(\varepsilon^4). \quad (9.38h)$$

It can be verified that if $v_{11} = -2$ and the rest of the μ_{rs} and v_{rs} are zero, these series agree with those given in Section 9.3 for the characteristic numbers of the Mathieu equation.

The application of these results to particular systems can be conveniently illustrated by considering the stability of two variable-parameter torsional systems. The first of these† consists of an inertia load driven through a Hooke's joint by means of torsionally flexible shafting. By using the transformation (9.5), the linearised equation governing the stability of this system can be written in the form

$$
\frac{d^2x}{d\tau^2} + \lambda[1 + (-\rho\cos 2\tau)\varepsilon + \{(-\tfrac{1}{8}\rho + \tfrac{1}{2}\rho^2) + (-\tfrac{1}{2}\rho)\cos 2\tau
$$
$$
+ (-\tfrac{3}{8}\rho + \tfrac{1}{2}\rho^2)\cos 4\tau\}\varepsilon^2 + \{(-\tfrac{1}{8}\rho + \tfrac{1}{2}\rho^2)
$$
$$
+ (-\tfrac{3}{8}\rho + \tfrac{5}{8}\rho^2 - \tfrac{3}{4}\rho^3)\cos 2\tau + (-\tfrac{3}{8}\rho + \tfrac{1}{2}\rho^2)\cos \tau
$$
$$
+ (-\tfrac{1}{8}\rho + \tfrac{3}{8}\rho^2 - \tfrac{1}{4}\rho^3)\cos 6\tau\}\varepsilon^3]x + O(\varepsilon^4) = 0. \tag{9.39}
$$

In this equation, x is a measure of the twist in the input shaft to the Hooke's joint, ρ is a shaft stiffness parameter, ε is a function of the angular misalignment of the input and output shafts, $\tau = \Omega t$, and $\lambda = \omega_n^2/\Omega^2$, where Ω is the rotational speed and ω_n the undamped natural frequency of the system. The coefficient of x in equation (9.39) has a period of π in τ due to the fact that the velocity-ratio of the Hooke's joint varies with a frequency of two cycles per revolution.

Now equation (9.39) is a Hill's equation of the type (9.37) in which

$$
\mu_{10} = 0, \quad \mu_{11} = -\rho; \quad \mu_{20} = -\tfrac{1}{8}\rho + \tfrac{1}{2}\rho^2, \quad \mu_{21} = -\tfrac{1}{2}\rho,
$$
$$
\mu_{22} = -\tfrac{3}{8}\rho + \tfrac{1}{2}\rho^2; \quad \mu_{30} = -\tfrac{1}{8}\rho + \tfrac{1}{2}\rho^2,
$$
$$
\mu_{31} = -\tfrac{3}{8}\rho + \tfrac{5}{8}\rho^2 - \tfrac{3}{4}\rho^3, \quad \mu_{32} = -\tfrac{3}{8}\rho + \tfrac{1}{2}\rho^2,
$$
$$
\mu_{33} = -\tfrac{1}{8}\rho + \tfrac{3}{8}\rho^2 - \tfrac{1}{4}\rho^3;
$$

and $v_{rs} = 0$ $(r, s \leqslant 3)$. Thus, substituting these parameter values into the series (9.38) indicates that the characteristic numbers for the Hooke's joint system are

$$
\tilde{a}_0 = 0 + O(\varepsilon^4),
$$
$$
\tilde{a}_1 = 1 + \tfrac{1}{2}\rho\varepsilon + (\tfrac{3}{8}\rho - \tfrac{9}{32}\rho^2)\varepsilon^2 + (\tfrac{5}{16}\rho - \tfrac{63}{128}\rho^2 - \tfrac{9}{512}\rho^3)\varepsilon^3
$$
$$
+ O(\varepsilon^4),
$$
$$
\tilde{b}_1 = 1 - \tfrac{1}{2}\rho\varepsilon + (-\tfrac{1}{8}\rho - \tfrac{9}{32}\rho^2)\varepsilon^2 + (-\tfrac{1}{16}\rho - \tfrac{9}{128}\rho^2 + \tfrac{9}{512}\rho^3)\varepsilon^3
$$
$$
+ O(\varepsilon^4),
$$
$$
\tilde{a}_2 = 4 + (\tfrac{5}{4}\rho - \tfrac{4}{3}\rho^2)\varepsilon^2 + (\tfrac{5}{4}\rho - \tfrac{4}{3}\rho^2)\varepsilon^3 + O(\varepsilon^4),
$$
$$
\tilde{b}_2 = 4 + (-\tfrac{1}{4}\rho - \tfrac{4}{3}\rho^2)\varepsilon^2 + (-\tfrac{1}{4}\rho - \tfrac{4}{3}\rho^2)\varepsilon^3 + O(\varepsilon^4),
$$
$$
\tilde{a}_3 = 9 + (\tfrac{9}{8}\rho - \tfrac{207}{64}\rho^2)\varepsilon^2 + (\tfrac{27}{16}\rho - \tfrac{387}{128}\rho^2 + \tfrac{9}{512}\rho^3)\varepsilon^3 + O(\varepsilon^4),
$$
$$
\tilde{b}_3 = 9 + (\tfrac{9}{8}\rho - \tfrac{207}{64}\rho^2)\varepsilon^2 + (\tfrac{9}{16}\rho - \tfrac{441}{128}\rho^2 - \tfrac{9}{512}\rho^3)\varepsilon^3 + O(\varepsilon^4),
$$

and so on for $\tilde{a}_4, \tilde{b}_4, \ldots$.

† See B. Porter, A theoretical analysis of the torsional oscillation of a system incorporating a Hooke's joint, *J. mech. Engng Sci.*, 3, 324, 1961.

Since it is physically impossible for λ to be negative, it is apparent that the domain of instability corresponding to $\lambda \leqslant \tilde{a}_0$ has no physical significance in this case. However, if the speed parameter $\lambda = \omega_n^2/\Omega^2$ lies between any of the pairs of values given by $(\tilde{a}_m, \tilde{b}_m)$ $(m = 1, 2, 3, \ldots)$, the solutions of equation (9.39) become unbounded, indicating that the Hooke's joint system will then oscillate violently. Since the leading terms in the series for $\tilde{a}_m$ and $\tilde{b}_m$ are both equal to m^2, it is evident that if ε is small these speed ranges of instability will lie near the values $\lambda = \omega_n^2/\Omega^2 = m^2$ $(m = 1, 2, 3, \ldots)$, i.e., near the speeds $\Omega = \omega_n/m$ $(m = 1, 2, 3, \ldots)$. Thus, the variable velocity-ratio of the Hooke's joint induces instability at speeds near integral sub-multiples of the natural frequency of torsional vibration of the system.

The second illustrative system† is the crankshaft of an idealised single-cylinder reciprocating machine. In this system the instabilities are caused by periodic inertia variations arising from piston reciprocation, rather than by variations in velocity-ratio as in the previous example. The transformation (9.5) can be used to show that the linearised equation governing the stability of this variable-inertia system can be written in the form

$$
\frac{d^2x}{d\tau^2} + [\lambda\{1 + (\cos 2\tau)\varepsilon + (\tfrac{1}{2} + \tfrac{1}{2}\cos 4\tau)\varepsilon^2 + (\tfrac{3}{4}\cos 2\tau
$$
$$
+ \tfrac{1}{4}\cos 6\tau)\varepsilon^3\} + (\tfrac{1}{2} - \tfrac{1}{2}\cos 4\tau)\varepsilon^2 + (\tfrac{1}{2}\cos 2\tau - \tfrac{1}{2}\cos 6\tau)\varepsilon^3]x
$$
$$
+ O(\varepsilon^4) = 0, \tag{9.40}
$$

if the length of the connecting rod is assumed to be infinite. In this equation, x is a measure of the twist in the crankshaft, ε is a dimensionless inertia-variation parameter, $\tau = \Omega t$, and $\lambda = \omega_n^2/\Omega^2$, where Ω is the rotational speed and ω_n the undamped natural frequency of the system. The coefficient of x in equation (9.40) has a period of π in τ because the inertia of the system varies with a frequency of two cycles per crankshaft revolution.

Equation (9.40) is a Hill's equation of the type (9.37) in which

$$\mu_{10} = 0, \quad \mu_{11} = 1; \quad \mu_{20} = \tfrac{1}{2}, \quad \mu_{21} = 0, \quad \mu_{22} = \tfrac{1}{4};$$
$$\mu_{30} = 0, \quad \mu_{31} = \tfrac{3}{4}, \quad \mu_{32} = 0, \quad \mu_{33} = \tfrac{1}{4}; \quad v_{10} = 0,$$
$$v_{11} = 0; \quad v_{20} = \tfrac{1}{2}, \quad v_{21} = 0, \quad v_{22} = -\tfrac{1}{2}; \quad v_{30} = 0,$$
$$v_{31} = \tfrac{1}{2}, \quad v_{32} = 0, \quad v_{33} = -\tfrac{1}{2}.$$

† See R. W. Gregory, Non-linear oscillation of a system having variable inertia, Ph.D. thesis, University of Durham, 1954.

With these values of the parameters, the series (9.38) for the character-istic numbers become

$$\tilde{a}_0 = -\tfrac{1}{2}\varepsilon^2 + O(\varepsilon^4),$$

$$\tilde{a}_1 = 1 - \tfrac{1}{2}\varepsilon - \tfrac{25}{32}\varepsilon^2 + \tfrac{25}{512}\varepsilon^3 + O(\varepsilon^4),$$

$$\tilde{b}_1 = 1 + \tfrac{1}{2}\varepsilon - \tfrac{25}{32}\varepsilon^2 - \tfrac{25}{512}\varepsilon^3 + O(\varepsilon^4),$$

$$\tilde{a}_2 = 4 - \tfrac{19}{12}\varepsilon^2 + O(\varepsilon^4),$$

$$\tilde{b}_2 = 4 - \tfrac{25}{12}\varepsilon^2 + O(\varepsilon^4),$$

$$\tilde{a}_3 = 9 - \tfrac{239}{64}\varepsilon^2 - \tfrac{25}{512}\varepsilon^3 + O(\varepsilon^4),$$

$$\tilde{b}_3 = 9 - \tfrac{239}{64}\varepsilon^2 + \tfrac{25}{512}\varepsilon^3 + O(\varepsilon^4),$$

and so on for $\tilde{a}_4$, $\tilde{b}_4$, ...

Since it is again physically impossible for λ to be negative, the domain of instability corresponding to $\lambda \leqslant \tilde{a}_0$ has no physical significance. However, if the speed is such that λ lies within any one of the closed intervals $(\tilde{a}_m, \tilde{b}_m)$ ($m = 1, 2, 3, \ldots$), the solutions of (9.40) become unbounded and the crankshaft will then execute violent vibrations. These speed ranges of instability again lie near the values $\Omega = \omega_n/m$ ($m = 1, 2, 3, \ldots$). However, of this infinity of speed ranges, only those corresponding to $m = 1$ and $m = 2$ are wide enough to have real practical significance, particularly when the effects of damping are taken into account.

Other types of generalised Mathieu equations have been studied extensively—for example, the Meissner equation in which the periodic term, $f(t)$, in Hill's equation has the form of a square wave. However, in all cases the boundaries of the domains of instability can be deter-mined (at least approximately) by calculating the appropriate character-istic numbers by the techniques described in Section 9.3.

Problems

1. Two identical compound pendula are suspended from a common support which is subjected to a vertical oscillatory motion given by $f(t) = a \cos \Omega t$.† Each pendulum is of mass m and of radius of gyra-tion ρ about its centre of gravity and is suspended at a distance c from its centre of gravity. The pendula are coupled together by a spring of stiffness k whose point of attachment to each pendulum is a distance b from the appropriate point of suspension. If the angular

† C. S. Hsu, On a restricted class of coupled Hill's equations and some applica-tions, *J. appl. Mech.*, **28**, 551, 1961.

displacements of the pendula from the downward vertical are assumed to remain small and are denoted by x_1 and x_2, the equations of motion of the system can be written in the approximate form

$$\frac{d^2x_1}{dt^2} + \left[\frac{cg}{\rho^2} + \frac{kb^2}{m\rho^2} + \frac{ca\Omega^2}{\rho^2}\cos\Omega t\right]x_1 - \frac{kb^2}{m\rho^2}x_2 = 0,$$

$$\left.\frac{d^2x_2}{dt^2} + \left[\frac{cg}{\rho^2} + \frac{kb^2}{m\rho^2} + \frac{ca\Omega^2}{\rho^2}\cos\Omega t\right]x_2 - \frac{kb^2}{m\rho^2}x_1 = 0. \right\}$$

By introducing new variables defined by $z_1 = x_1 + x_2, z_2 = x_1 - x_2$, and a new time variable $\tau = \Omega t/2$, show that these coupled equations in x_1 and x_2 become two decoupled Mathieu equations in z_1 and z_2. Hence show that, if a is small, the coupled pendula will become unstable near the frequencies

$$\Omega = \frac{2\Omega_k}{n} \quad (k = 1, 2; \ n = 1, 2, 3, \ldots),$$

where

$$\Omega_1^2 = \frac{cg}{\rho^2}, \qquad \Omega_2^2 = \frac{cg}{\rho^2}\left[1 + \frac{2kb^2}{mcg}\right].$$

What is the physical significance of the quantities Ω_1 and Ω_2?

2. The equation governing the small lateral vibrations of a uniform string of length l and mass per unit length m, which is fixed at each end and subjected to a time-dependent tension $F(t)$, has the form†

$$m\frac{\partial^2 u}{\partial t^2} = F(t)\frac{\partial^2 u}{\partial x^2},$$

where $u(x, t)$ is the lateral displacement at a distance x from one end of the string at time t. If u is expressed as the series

$$u(x, t) = \sum_{k=1}^{\infty} z_k(t) \sin\frac{k\pi x}{l},$$

and if

$$F(t) = P + H\cos\Omega t \quad (P > 0),$$

show that the $z_k(t)$ satisfy equations of the form

$$\frac{d^2z_k}{dt^2} + \Omega_k^2\left[1 + \frac{H}{P}\cos\Omega t\right]z_k = 0 \quad (k = 1, 2, 3, \ldots),$$

where the

$$\Omega_k^2 = \frac{k^2\pi^2 P}{ml^2}$$

† S. Lubkin and J. J. Stoker, Stability of columns and strings under periodically varying forces, *Q. appl. Math.*, **1**, 215, 1943.

are the squares of the undamped natural frequencies of free lateral vibration of the string when $H = 0$. Transform the equations for the $z_k(t)$ into standard Mathieu equations by introducing a new time variable, and hence show that the string will become unstable near the frequencies

$$\Omega = \frac{2\Omega_k}{n} \quad (n, k = 1, 2, 3, \ldots)$$

if H/P is small.

3. A uniform vertical shaft of non-circular cross-section rotates at a constant speed Ω and is constrained in such a way that flexural vibrations can occur only in a fixed vertical plane containing the shaft axis: the equation governing such vibrations has the form†

$$[C_0 + C(t)]\frac{\partial^4 u}{\partial x^4} = -m\frac{\partial^2 u}{\partial t^2},$$

where m is the mass per unit length of the shaft, C_0 is the mean flexural rigidity, $C(t)$ is a periodic function of t giving the variation of effective rigidity with rotation, and $u(x, t)$ is the lateral displacement of the shaft at a section defined by the axial coordinate x at time t. The stability of this system, for any set of boundary conditions, can be investigated by expressing u as the series

$$u(x, t) = \sum_{k=1}^{\infty} z_k(t)\phi_k(x),$$

where the $\phi_k(x)$ define the shapes of the normal modes of transverse shaft vibration when $C(t) = 0$: the $\phi_k(x)$ thus constitute an orthogonal set and satisfy equations of the form

$$C_0 \frac{d^4\phi_k}{dx^4} = m\Omega_k^2 \phi_k \ (k = 1, 2, 3, \ldots)$$

where Ω_k is the natural frequency of the kth normal mode. If $C(t) = \alpha C_0 \cos m\Omega t$, where m is an even integer, show that the $z_k(t)$ satisfy equations of the form

$$\frac{d^2 z_k}{dt^2} + \Omega_k^2(1 + \alpha \cos m\Omega t)z_k = 0 \quad (k = 1, 2, 3, \ldots)$$

and that these equations can be transformed into standard Mathieu equations by introducing a new time variable. Hence show that the shaft will become unstable near the speeds

$$\Omega = \frac{2\Omega_k}{mn} \quad (k, n = 1, 2, 3, \ldots)$$

if α is small.

† C. S. Hsu, loc. cit.

4. The vibrations of the side-rod drive system of an electric locomotive
are governed by a Hill's equation of the form†

$$J \frac{d^2x}{dt^2} + \psi(\Omega t)x = 0,$$

where J is the effective moment of inertia of the system, Ω is the
angular velocity of the electric motor, and $\psi(\Omega t)$ is the periodically
varying stiffness of the system. The latter function is given by

$$\psi(\Omega t) = \frac{a + b \cos 2\Omega t + c \cos 4\Omega t}{p + q \cos 2\Omega t + r \cos 4\Omega t},$$

where the parameters a, b, c, p, q, r are functions of the elastic characteristics of the system. If b, c, q and r are small compared with a and
p, and if

$$\frac{a}{Jp} = \rho_0, \qquad \frac{b}{Jp} = \rho_1\varepsilon, \qquad \frac{c}{Jp} = \rho_2\varepsilon, \qquad \frac{q}{p} = \rho_3\varepsilon, \qquad \frac{r}{p} = \rho_4\varepsilon,$$

where ε is a small parameter, show that the system governing equation can be expressed in the form

$$\frac{d^2x}{dt^2} + \rho_0[1 + \varepsilon(a_1 \cos 2\Omega t + a_2 \cos 4\Omega t)$$

$$+ \varepsilon^2(a_3 \cos 2\Omega t + a_4 \cos 4\Omega t + a_5 \cos 6\Omega t$$
$$+ a_6 \cos 8\Omega t) + \dots]x = 0,$$

where

$$a_1 = \frac{\rho_1 - \rho_3\rho_0}{\rho_0}, \qquad a_2 = \frac{\rho_2 - \rho_4\rho_0}{\rho_0},$$

$$a_3 = \frac{2\rho_3\rho_4\rho_0 - \rho_1\rho_4 - \rho_2\rho_3}{2\rho_0},$$

and so on. Hence deduce that the system will become unstable near
the speeds

$$\Omega = \frac{\rho_0^{\frac{1}{2}}}{n} \quad (n = 1, 2, 3, \dots).$$

In particular, show that the critical speed range corresponding to
$n = 1$ is defined by

$$1 - \tfrac{1}{2}a_1\varepsilon + \tfrac{1}{96}(21a_1^2 - 4a_2^2 - 6a_1a_2 - 48a_3)\varepsilon^2 + \dots \leqslant \frac{\rho_0}{\Omega^2}$$

$$\leqslant 1 + \tfrac{1}{2}a_1\varepsilon + \tfrac{1}{96}(21a_1^2 - 4a_2^2 + 6a_1a_2 + 48a_3)\varepsilon^2 + \dots.$$

* S. Timoshenko, *Vibration problems in engineering*, p. 167, Constable, 1937.

INDEX